RICE UNIVERSITY

SEMICENTENNIAL PUBLICATIONS

Perspectives
in Medieval History

EDITORS

KATHERINE FISCHER DREW

FLOYD SEYWARD LEAR

CONTRIBUTORS

S. HARRISON THOMSON

LYNN WHITE, JR.

A. C. CROMBIE

GAINES POST

E. DWIGHT SALMON

Perspectives

in

Medieval

History

PUBLISHED FOR

WILLIAM MARSH RICE UNIVERSITY

BY

THE UNIVERSITY OF CHICAGO PRESS

Library of Congress Catalog Card Number: 63-20902

THE UNIVERSITY OF CHICAGO PRESS, CHICAGO & LONDON
The University of Toronto Press, Toronto 5, Canada

Preface

THE ESSAYS contained in this volume were originally presented as a special series of five lectures sponsored by the history department of Rice University as part of its contribution to the activities celebrating the Rice University Semicentennial. It is the general purpose of this series to evaluate the state and condition of medieval studies in this country at the present time and to show how, in the light of recent research and new interpretations, the medieval has influenced, conditioned, and shaped the modern age. Limitations of time and circumstance have restricted the range of these studies to a few well-defined areas, but it is hoped that, within the range represented here, a clear presentation of new emphases and relations has been made.

S. Harrison Thomson begins with a historiographical survey of medieval study in America from the time of Henry Charles Lea to the present, in which he shows the rise of a peculiarly native American interest in this area. Thereafter the impact of German ideals of scholarship introduced a rigor and a precision into the discipline that it has never lost. He indicates the influence of both world wars on medieval study, the great, constructive, new developments of the interwar period, characterized by the work of such distinguished American medievalists as Charles Homer Haskins, Dana Carleton Munro, and Lynn Thorndike, and finally the contributions of European émigrés since World War II, with their high linguistic competence and specialized abilities. In addition, he notes the chronological continuity of early American thought and institutions with the later Middle Ages and the peculiar direct indebtedness of Americans to their medieval forebears, an indebtedness that makes it highly appropriate for American scholarship to lend its attention to medieval study.

The paper by Lynn White, Jr., synthesizes a wide range of disparate matter culled from those aspects of medieval technology that he has made his special field of research. He shows that the Middle Ages were never as static and unreceptive to change in material concerns as conventional views have represented them. He indicates also the great variety of contacts with remote regions and cultures and their reciprocal influences. The vertical process of continuing change and flexibility from early medieval times deep into the modern age is stressed. Indeed, the very concept "medieval" loses specific meaning as it becomes increasingly difficult to establish limits within which to fix a true middle period. Further he points to the rarity of genuine discontinuities in history.

A. C. Crombie places the role of science in the Middle Ages in new perspective. He shows that the revisions made necessary by recent research, much of it original in his own work, cannot be accommodated within the traditional and customary framework of medieval civilization. He traces the scientific movement from the collision of theological doctrine based on revelation with rational philosophic and scientific doctrines to the emergence of genuinely observational and experimental methods and finally to mathematical procedures essential to precise computation and measurement and exact description of phenomena. Much that has heretofore been accepted as specifically modern is shown to have its foundations in medieval thought, and consequently the modern debt to the medieval period is much greater than has been commonly recognized.

Although constitutional and legal studies belong to an old established field of medieval research reaching back into the nineteenth century, Gaines Post breaks new ground with a paper in the still relatively untilled area of the public law of the later Middle Ages. He develops his subject within the secular frame of reference apart from the more widely cultivated theology of the law. He traces the increasing powers of the state from their less well-defined feudal beginnings to their more nearly complete expression in the early modern national states. The process of becoming public is characterized by the appearance of "reason of state" as a central factor associated with emerging concepts of sovereignty. The new roles of kingship, estates, and parliamentary institutions are related to the new body politic, which belongs to the modern world. In this paper an old classical area of medieval study is made to yield returns that result from the changed approaches and emphases of present-day scholarship.

In the final essay E. Dwight Salmon brings to bear the perspective of long teaching experience of a scholar trained in early modern history. He reviews a considerable range of the new revisions of medieval history and shows their impact on modern history and historical thinking. He illustrates with significant detail many medieval trends and movements that have formed the modern world. He takes examples from methods of warfare both on land and on sea and examines the growth of a medieval world view based on increasing knowledge of distant lands and peoples. He shows the deep medieval forces that underlie the journeys of the overland travelers and the great voyages of exploration and discovery. Again one faces the inherent difficulty of periodizing medieval history because it shades imperceptibly into what we call the modern period and because these medieval processes oftentimes continue in our modern life.

It is the hope of Rice University that scholars will find in these studies ideas to engage their attention and that the general reader will find new matter to stir his interest. Above all, it is our hope that here added evidence will appear to support the position that the first president of the Mediaeval Academy of America expressed in his first presidential address in 1926. There Edward K. Rand gave a crushing rejoinder to those who would regard the Middle Ages as a time of gloom and uniformity. These papers reflect the newer, brighter view.

The editors of this volume are deeply indebted to the medievalists who have prepared these papers in the fields of their special competence. They are also appreciative of the unfailing support given them by the members of the Rice Semicentennial Committee in the arrangement of the public sessions at which the papers were presented and for their constant encouragement in the editorial work involved in getting the papers to the publisher.

K. F. DREW and F. S. LEAR

HOUSTON, TEXAS
June 1963

Contents

S. HARRISON THOMSON

The Growth of a Discipline: Medieval Studies in America

NEXT TO PROPHECY concerning his future, man has always been most interested in his past. History in all its manifold aspects has quite properly been a subject dear to human society. Everyone has a right to ask: Where do I come from? What were my forebears like? How did I get to be what I am? America has a special approach to history by reason of the fact that it has so many "pasts." Our multiple inheritance, from the many nations that have poured their sons and daughters into our melting pot, has laid upon us a unique obligation of curiosity about the pasts of all the peoples of the earth, for we count as Americans all those, from whatsoever land and tradition they may have come, who have chosen of their own volition to share our freedom and help to build our common future. A native of France, for example, is generally certain as well as justly proud of the fact that for many centuries his ancestors have also been Frenchmen. So also the Englishman, the German, the Italian, the Norwegian, and, in spite of mass dislocations brought on by wars and political changes, almost all the peoples of the earth. But, for our country (as in a less sensational degree for Australia and Canada, also lands of refuge and opportunity) this condition does not hold. One has only to look at a telephone book in any one of our larger cities—or, perhaps better, run his eye down the registration list of any college class of one hundred

S. HARRISON THOMSON is Professor of History at the University of Colorado, where he has taught both medieval and Slavic history since 1936. He is editor of the *Bulletin of Progress of Medieval and Renaissance Studies,* of *Medievalia et Humanistica,* and the *Journal of Central European Affairs.* Professor Thomson holds degrees from Princeton, Charles University in Prague, and Oxford. He was chief of the Office of War Information and special assistant to the American ambassador in Czechoslovakia in 1945 and director of the U.S. Information Service in Warsaw, Poland, in 1946. He has been a member of the Institute for Advanced Study at Princeton, a fellow of the Mediaeval Academy of America, and first vice-president of the Academy.

students—to realize that we are blessed with a national heterogeneity unparalleled in human history. This very national miscellaneousness is of direct relevance to the teaching of history throughout our whole educational system. If man is generically and incurably addicted to curiosity about his origins and his forebears, as a people we must, or we should, be interested in many pasts and many places of origin. No other Western people could possibly match the range of our curiosities in this direction. This built-in breadth presents opportunities as well as obligations. The opportunities lie in a residuum of special sympathy or interest presented by the existence among our citizenry of those with varied national backgrounds. Our obligations stem from the opportunities. Americans should be able to understand the stresses and strains, the ambitions and traditions of many peoples. The cry for understanding is abroad in the land, and this element of "internationalism" is present throughout our whole population. To paraphrase the Apostle Paul: neither Jew nor Greek, neither French nor English, but one supranational and truly international people—America. Potentially any American is himself a society of nations who, as an entity of mixed blood, should feel equally at home in Berlin or in Dublin, in Florence or in Warsaw. At this point we meet once again our opportunities and our obligations, and thus the subject of our immediate interest—the discipline of medieval studies in America and its growth.

The field of medieval studies, if not unique in its broad coverage, is at least remarkable for its breadth. Where the disciplines concerned with more recent times—politics, economics, sociology, philosophy, the vernacular languages and literatures—are, for the most part, limited to very special views of their subject matter, the medievalist tends to regard all these views as within his purview and for a period of about twelve hundred years. He may be optimistic in staking out so large a claim, but he holds to his breadth of view with laudable patience—perhaps "stubbornness" is a better term. The average textbook bearing the title *Medieval History*, destined for undergraduate consumption, will cover all aspects of European life and thought in the period, roughly, between A.D. 300 and A.D. 1500. The theology of the Church, heresy and mysticism, political thought, economic realities, the texture of society, the concepts of monarchy and empire, war and dynastic involvements, cathedral and cottage, art and architecture, diplomacy and court life, language and literature, agriculture and communication —all these are grist for the medievalist's mill. He can hardly be accused of modesty or narrowness.

Perhaps if we look deeper into the complex of the medievalist and the Middle Ages, we may be able to forgive him for his temerity in trying to understand so vast and variegated a field. At this point we

may properly point out that it was around the year 1500 that cata-
strophic changes in the world view of the European man occurred.
Three events of world-shaking significance took place within a few
years: the invention and spread of printing, the discovery of the New
World, and the Protestant Reformation. The old, self-contained, uni-
fied Europe, the home of our ancestors, was no longer. Our medievalist, then, in pursuit of the archetype from which he sprang, looking for it in intact purity, certainly feels that in the period before
1500 lie the answers to Western origins and thus the rewards of study.
There, he thinks, he finds Western civilization in its purest form. I
am trying to explain the smugness you encounter in the presence of
any committed medievalist. The field of medieval studies is broad and
comprehensive, and the medievalist is convinced that he is the proper
custodian of the secrets sought by the more modern disciplines. He is
probably right.

   Since about 1500, America and Europe may have gone separate
ways, but in America the student of the Middle Ages can look back
on these same three crucial events and feel that they form a division
point that allows him to approach the antecedent period on a basis of
equality with his European colleague. What took place before 1500 is
as much the American scholar's domain as it is that of the native
French, German, or Italian guildsman. The medieval Church, the
Holy Roman Empire, chivalry, and the Gothic cathedral—these are
our heritage as well as our European colleagues'. For a student of the
Middle Ages in an America with a strong Protestant tradition, the
question of Catholic or Protestant does not properly exist. All our
ancestors before the Reformation lived and died under one mother
church. The Protestant scholar of the Middle Ages who forgets this
fact is handicapping himself and is likely to pervert the story he tells.
On the other hand, a Catholic scholar who regards the Middle Ages as
his special province is guilty of an equally serious mistake.

   Distance from the events can have a further advantage. Whereas a
native French scholar writing in 1963 about the struggle between
France and England in the fourteenth and fifteenth centuries would
inevitably feel impelled to present clearly and, of course, fairly the
French case, an American scholar should, ideally, be able to present a
story approaching definitive objectivity. He could hardly, as Germans
were urged during the Nazi regime, "think with his blood." His blood
might be so mixed—French, German, Scottish, and Swiss, say—that he
would long since have given up trying to balance his feelings; he
would end up thinking as an American. The American scholar may
be in a better position to see European history straight and true than
his European colleague, for remoteness from the heat of battle can be

counted a great advantage for the American medievalist, and we would do well not to minimize its value. Whether or not, in the past, we have adequately realized our position may be another question. By virtue of being supranational guildsmen, we should have been able to tell the story of the Middle Ages more truly and also more comprehensively than any other Western people. It is my purpose to look into both performance and development in an effort to assess our progress, to ascertain, perhaps, where we now stand and what, most obviously, we need to do in order to realize our opportunities and fulfil our obligations.

It is customary to regard World War I as the beginning of medieval studies in America, and with some justification. That war certainly marks a period of amazing expansion in this area. Over two and a quarter million young Americans spent impressionable time on European soil and inevitably were deeply moved by what they saw and learned. It was America's mass return to the land of its fathers—England, France, Germany, or Italy. On their return to our shores, many of them changed the course of their education, which had been interrupted by military service, and the curricula of colleges and universities were perforce altered and expanded to satisfy their demands. There was, for example, a great upsurge in the study of French civilization, art, literature, and language, which required substantial faculty adjustments. Despite the importance of this period, however, we would do a great injustice to the pioneers of medieval studies in America if we were to rest our inquiry there and neglect the preceding decades. Indeed, let it be quickly said, some of our greatest work in medieval studies began or was completed before 1914.

We may pass over some nineteenth-century American scholars—for example, Washington Irving, William H. Prescott, and James Motley—as being in many ways more European than American. But when we come to Henry Charles Lea (1825–1909), we are confronted by a personality who satisfies in every respect the specifications of an American. He was an amateur historian, a senior partner in a successful Philadelphia publishing house, active in civic affairs, and a connoisseur of real estate. He published eighteen volumes of work on the medieval church, the Inquisition in the Middle Ages, in Spain and her colonies, celibacy of the clergy, confession and indulgences, and many articles on ecclesiastical law, all this between 1858 and his death in 1909. Not a page of them but may now be read with profit and most of them, based on primary sources, remain fundamental for the history of the Middle Ages. Recognized with amazement by foreign scholars as epoch-making, Lea's work gave America a reputation for historical scholarship hardly deserved by the general level of performance on this side of the Atlantic at the time. In all truth Lea was, by himself, an epoch in American historiography of the Middle Ages. Lord Acton asserted of Lea's *History of the Inquisition of the Middle Ages* that it was "the most important contribution of the new world to the religious history of the old." Though offered many professorships and honorary degrees, Lea was never a teaching member of the profession. His work, brilliant, solid, immense, imaginative, and definitive, was for the whole wide world of learning. It reached beyond what we properly speak of as the historical discipline yet was an earnest of what America was capable of producing.

In the last years of Lea's life, that is, from the last decade of the nineteenth century to the outbreak of war in 1914, there were at our colleges and universities some individuals interested in various aspects of medieval life and thought. Perusing the tables of contents of such professional journals as *Modern Language Notes, Transactions* (later *Publications*) *of the Modern Language Association*, the *Journal of English and Germanic Philology*, and the *American Historical Review*, one notes a not inconsiderable number of studies on medieval subjects. Matters of philological or etymological interest, attempts to trace relations between literatures or individuals, conjectures as to manuscript readings, and biographical studies made up the major part of the medieval production in these years.

It is also to be noted that during these years the most precise methodology can be related in some way to Germany. Many of the more ambitious young American scholars, attracted by the world renown of German *Wissenschaft*, had gone to German universities to study and, hopefully, to obtain German doctorates. Even in the American universities that offered graduate work, such as Johns Hopkins and Harvard, there was a tendency to adopt German methods and, if I may say so, the German approach. Many scholars working in English literature and philology, and hardly fewer in Romance literature and philology, were anxious to study in a German university. Berlin, Leipzig, Bonn, Erlangen, Halle, Heidelberg, and Tübingen were full of Americans preparing to man our college and university teaching staffs: a German degree was thought to be an open sesame to a successful academic career. There is no doubt the American could and did learn something from German scientific rigor, and the effects of this schooling upon our own academic curricula were to be long lasting, though not always beneficial.

One important ingredient of enduring scholarship was frequently lacking in the German tradition: humility in the face of the subject matter. Lea had that virtue to a high degree, and it alone almost explains his greatness. Some American medievalists active in these pre-1914 years either were not exposed to German *Wissenschaft* or, if so exposed, resisted its pomposity and its occasional blindness. George Lincoln Burr, for example, studied at Leipzig, but also at Paris; and being a bookman born, he had little respect for the German's ignorance of anything published outside Germany. His own wide interests and his inspiring teaching made Cornell a center of curiosity (sometimes called "research") about the mind and ethics of the Middle Ages. Ludwig Traube of Munich, classicist and paleographer, attracted a unique group of young American classicists in the first decade of this century: Edward K. Rand, Charles A. Beeson, E. A. Lowe, Charles U. Clark, and B. L. Ullman, all names now high in the firmament of American medieval scholarship. Traube inculcated in all he taught candor, probity, consuming curiosity, humility, and patience. His influence on American medievalism was completely beneficial and has entered into the very fabric of our discipline.

Indeed other benefits to American medieval studies derived from this German tutelage. The Germans possessed certain technical controls necessary to the complete mastery of the humanities. In every German university there were likely to be seminars in the auxiliary sciences: paleography and diplomatic, *Textbildung*, historiography, comparative philology, philosophy of history, bibliography, heraldry, numismatics and sphragistics, chronology, criticism of sources, and other technical specializations dear to the German heart. Many American medievalists were exposed to this battery of disciplines, and probably, over all, they benefited. There remains no doubt that many of these wandering scholars did, on their return, quite justly attain positions of eminence and leadership on the American academic scene. Without a familiarity with these techniques, competition with German scholarship would have been impossible and consequent liberation from its heavy hand inconceivable. We have therefore to be doubly grateful for this pre-1914 Germanic instruction, first, because its disciplinary effects were necessary before American academic scholarship could stand on its own feet and, second, because the period of indoctrination did not last long enough to become a fixture.

The war period, 1914–19, witnessed a profound change in the spirit of American academe. If a year abroad at a German university had previously been the style among ambitious young academicians, a sort of guarantee of recognition by their fellows, Germany was not so attractive after 1919. The earlier assumption of German *Objektivität* and the Teutonic profession of scientific quest of truth had been shaken by the proclamation in October, 1914, by ninety-two German professors, at whose feet so many Americans had studied, that the invasion of Belgium was completely justified. Perhaps, after all, German truth left something to be desired. The leaders of education in England, France, and Belgium took advantage of the situation and began to make accommodations for American graduate students. At the end of the war, the tide began to flow to Paris, Oxford, Ghent, and even to Italy. Oxford hurriedly and somewhat reluctantly set up a doctoral program. The Sorbonne, traditionally a cosmopolitan institution, had less difficulty in absorbing the numbers of eager Americans that crowded the Left Bank. There were berets everywhere, seldom worn by Frenchmen.

In our colleges and universities, the interest in things German nearly vanished, and almost overnight enthusiasm for things French grew miraculously. Whereas, before the war, beginning classes in German had enrolled one hundred students and the German department had been large and busy, suddenly there were beginning classes of only fifteen or twenty and the professors were freed for research and conversation. French classes were large; capable and trained instructors were hard to come by; and *la civilisation française* was everywhere the thing, trailed at no great distance by English culture and institutions.

Graduate work and published research followed the same pattern. Medieval studies in the literature, language, history, education, art, and society of the Romance and early Anglo-Saxon world sprang to life. This new focus of interest meant that a complete reorientation of direction and implementation was called for. There was a shortage of competent, mature scholars. There were tremendous gaps in library holdings, even in the best equipped institutions, and many worthy projects, good in themselves, had to be abandoned or postponed for lack of proper guidance and the tools of research.

There were gaps and there were shortages in view of the vastly heightened demands, but there was also a considerable reserve of scholars who knew Europe from study and commerce with their European colleagues. Among them were some who realized the needs and knew in what direction the profession should go. It will suffice to name only a few, in order to bring to mind the quality of scholar on whose shoulders the task of guidance rested. At Harvard, E. K. Rand in classics and medieval Latin tradition, C. H. Grandgent in medieval Italian and Latin language and literature, G. L. Kittredge in Romance philology, Charles Gross in English economic history, and C. H. Haskins in medieval culture were a formidable company. At Yale were George Burton Adams and Sidney Mitchell, both in English institutional history. At Vassar was James F. Baldwin in English constitutional history and, at Columbia, Lynn Thorndike in the history of medieval science. At Mount Holyoke College, there was Miss Nellie Neilson in English legal and economic history. At Princeton, Dana Carleton Munro in the Crusades, Allan Marquand and Charles Rufus Morey in medieval and Renaissance art, and E. C. Armstrong in medieval French literature were masters of their arts. Chicago had James Westfall Thompson in history, William A. Nitze in medieval French literature, Philip S. Allen in medieval Latin poetry, and John Manly in medieval English literature. At Berkeley was Louis J. Paetow in medieval education and, at Iowa, B. L. Ullman in the classic tradition and the humanistic Renaissance. Many more could be, and probably should be, named, but all these, at least, were scholars of international stature, recognized abroad, with definitive *opera* to their credit, able to command respect in any company. With leadership of this quality, widely spread institutionally and in key positions, medieval studies could hope for an assured future.

The new situation precipitated by the war and its aftermath was quickly realized by these leaders. In December, 1920, at the annual meeting of the Modern Language Association, Professor Manly, in his presidential address, called for a reorganization of the meetings of the association to stimulate and recognize specialized research. The next year one whole session was devoted to "The Influence of Latin Culture on Medieval Culture." Those present hopefully organized themselves as a permanent group, which soon became a national movement (sectionalized in academic fashion into East, Middle West, and Pacific Coast) under the over-all chairmanship of E. K. Rand of Harvard. The movement met a widespread welcome, and scholars with various interests centered in the Middle Ages who had hitherto felt isolated or in a vacuum responded enthusiastically to the appeal for support. The group put itself under the wing of a larger and established body of scholars and became the Committee on Medieval Latin Studies of the American Council of Learned Societies.

The first task the committee set itself was, quite properly, an assessment of the status of medieval Latin studies in America. It soon developed that the interests of many scholars went beyond the original area of medieval Latin culture and that there was a lively demand for a more comprehensive grouping embracing scholarship in classics, history, art, law, philosophy, and vernacular languages and literatures. I am honored to add that much of the data on which the committee based its assessment of the present and future of medieval studies was accumulated and reported by my predecessor at the University of Colorado, James F. Willard, who, in 1924, published the first *Bulletin of Progress of Medieval Studies in the United States of America*. This first bulletin listed sixty scholars in this field, and the number was to multiply many fold in a few years. From this point of assessment to the formal incorporation of the Mediaeval Academy of America in December, 1925, and the inception of *Speculum: A Journal of Mediaeval Studies* in January, 1926, was only a short step.

The existence of a publishing medium and a formal organization specifically directed to medieval studies was enthusiastically received by all who had found the area challenging and satisfying. Those who had been laboring in the darkness of isolation saw the great light of a new day. Indeed, the title of Professor Rand's first presidential address not inappropriately contained the words "mediaeval gloom." Equally appropriately, the accompanying address, by the noted architect Ralph Adams Cram, looked forward. Its title was "The Mediaeval Academy and Modern Life."

Somewhat surprisingly, at the annual meeting of the American Catholic Historical Association in the year of the founding of the Mediaeval Academy, no paper on a medieval subject was read, but this oversight has since been abundantly remedied. From that time, I think I am safe in saying, no reputable learned society concerned with the cultural history of the West has failed to include the Middle Ages in its purview. A sample comparison of the number of books on medieval subjects published just before and soon after the foundation of the Academy would substantiate this increasing interest. In 1925, American scholars published twenty-four books in the medieval field. In 1928, the number reached sixty-four. There began also a growth—less easily reduced to figures—in offerings at the college and university level. In 1925, there were 120 doctoral theses announced as in progress or completed; in 1932, 380; in 1940, 432. Obviously, the announcement of titles and their completion are not the same thing. But they were not the same thing in 1925 either. Yet, lest anyone think that the Mediaeval Academy was solely responsible for the upsurge or for any heightened quality of the production in this field, let it be pointed out that most of the classic works that appeared in the twenties and thirties were either produced, planned, or on the way before 1926.

That perpetually inspiring work of Henry Osborn Taylor, *The Mediaeval Mind*, first appeared in 1911. Rand's study *The Script of Tours* was the result of years of work going back to the 1900's. Volume I of Lynn Thorndike's monumental *History of Magic and Experimental Science* was published in 1923 but had been implicit in his doctoral thesis, formulated in 1902. Haskins' magisterial *Studies in the History of Mediaeval Science*, which first appeared as a book in 1924, was a felicitous assembling of studies going back a full decade to pre-1914 times. The same could be said of the work of J. P. Tatlock in medieval English literature, of J. M. Manly on Chaucer, of George

P. T. Flom in medieval Scandinavian literature, of B. L. Ullman and the classical tradition in the Renaissance, of D. C. Munro and the Crusades, and of E. A. Lowe and his studies in early medieval Latin paleography.

There were not a few others—masters of their trade or capable of being masters—well equipped by research, travel, and actual publication to guide disciples or to sit in judgment on work done either in America or abroad. What was needed in the mid-twenties was some coalescence of interest, a focusing on the field with consequent delimitations, a clear and objective assessment of specific needs and objectives, and an academic encouragement to new workers in the métier. The Mediaeval Academy, guided by men of caliber and vision, was admirably adapted by reason of its origin and composition to satisfy most of these needs. By its very existence, it emphasized the presence of the many American scholars already productively at work and, by implication, it challenged younger scholars to carry on, to correct, or to complete the work so valiantly begun in this area.

On other scores the Academy was helpless. It could not fill the tremendous gaps in library holdings, and anyone planning work in this field at almost any university in the country soon became aware of them. Older works—incunabula and works published in the sixteenth, seventeenth, and eighteenth centuries—were often scarce in Europe and frequently unobtainable in the United States. If the subject of a scholar's research went beyond printed works to manuscripts he was likely, in these early years, to find that the European library in which his manuscripts reposed had no photographic facilities, and this might be the least of his difficulties. In the end, lacking time and funds to go to the spot, he might give up in despair. Many did, to the great damage of our academic performance.

Nevertheless, the challenge was there, but the twofold question arose in the mind of any younger aspirant as he mapped out that necessary compromise between his desires and inclinations on the one hand, and the realities of making a living on the other: Will I be able to get to Europe to study early European culture on the spot, as everybody tells me is necessary? Then, assuming I can do that, will I be able to publish the results of my research and get a teaching post in a college or university when I have done this necessary ground work? These related questions loomed large in the minds of young scholars as they surveyed the situation and planned their careers.

Obviously, even at best, not every ambition could be satisfied, but encouragement could be given. In the early twenties the Commission for Relief in Belgium thought it proper to offer fellowships to promising young American academicians. Some scholars who are today numbered among our leaders took advantage of this opportunity; and some Belgian universities, notably Ghent, the academic home of Henri Pirenne, welcomed American visitors. The happy results are still being felt today. A number of European ministries of education or culture, anxious to establish good will, set up modest fellowships for American scholars, hoping to store up credit, perhaps in heaven, for cultural sympathy. These grants were in all probability the wisest investment of capital that any smallish nation could have made. Most of these fellows were engaged in historical or literary studies; a number were in the Middle Ages; and the American academic scene has been greatly enriched by their sympathy and firsthand knowledge.

In 1925 there occurred another significant breakthrough for younger members of the medieval guild—the answer to one of their leading questions. The John Simon Guggenheim Foundation was set up with an announced program of scholarly aid to students in the humanities. This was a great boon to the guild, for a substantial number of young scholars, both predoctoral and postdoctoral, devotees of the Middle Ages in literature, the classics, art, music, history, and philosophy, were among the early Guggenheim Fellows. A great gain in prestige was promptly remarked; the field was beginning to be respectable. More was to come. In 1929, the American Council of Learned Societies announced fellowships in the humanities for 1930, and again a very substantial number of those chosen were addicts of the Middle Ages. I should not be willing to admit that the number so selected was in any way in improper proportion.

The results of these and like awards were soon increasingly evident in the curricula of the institutions to which these scholars returned, inspired, encouraged, greatly broadened, and confirmed in their enthusiasms by contact with their European equals and betters and, no less important, convinced of their own capacities to do work that would compare favorably with that of their foreign confreres. Puzzled and defenseless deans and department chairmen were faced with requests to allow the introduction of new courses in various aspects of medieval life and culture—intellectual history, philosophy, economic history, paleography, the history of the papacy, constitutional development, even medieval and Renaissance music. Librarians were swamped with requests for funds to purchase expensive sets— the *Monumenta Germaniae historica*, Migne's *Patrologiae*, *Early English Text Society*, *Société des anciens textes français*, other obscure series of archival material, long runs of hard-to-obtain journals —and even to provide space for seminar rooms. Their resistance was heroic, but they had to make some concessions, and today, somewhere in the United States, almost every important journal and monograph can be found. There are still gaps, of course. The original mystification of librarians in the presence of these urges was disturbing, as I can document from my own experience. In 1937, the librarian at my university was proudly showing me the floor plans for the new library we had been authorized to build. On the third floor there were rooms with no name written in. On a rash impulse, I took his pencil and wrote on one of these well-placed rooms *Studium paleographicum* and handed back his pencil. He looked at what I had written and exclaimed (and I quote): "What the hell is that?" I still have a *studium paleographicum*, and the librarian and I are on friendly terms.

In the period from 1920—that is, from Professor Manly's epochal appeal to the Modern Language Association and the immediate formation of the Committee on Medieval Latin Studies—until the outbreak of World War II in 1939, medieval studies in America grew in stature, breadth, confidence, competence, and favor with the educational world and, indeed, the general cultured public. Doctors of philosophy in the various fields of medieval studies were sought after and generally well received. From about 1934, as the fires of Nazism made life in Germany uncomfortable for independent-minded men, our profession was further enriched by imports from abroad. Many of these were first rate; others were less competent. A respectable number of them were medieval or Renaissance specialists, and many have added dimension to our profession, instructing our young and producing works of real value in their specialties. Without these new Americans, many of our colleges and universities would have been very shorthanded during the two decades when war and recovery occupied a whole generation of junior academicians. The postwar emigration from Central Europe brought us another group of men who have chosen freedom; and, fortified by their presence in a number of medieval and Renaissance fields, America can, with pride, count as hers the leading scholars in the world. Europe's loss has been our gain.

In this same period between the wars, several notable projects in medieval studies came to acknowledgeable fruition. C. R. Morey's *Index of Christian Art*, grand in conception and brilliant in execution, was widely recognized as an *opus eximium*, useful to scholars throughout the learned world. K. C. Conant's excavation of the Abbey of Cluny made notable progress, fed by high imagination and incredible special competence. *Studies in the Script of Tours*, by E. K. Rand aided by L. W. Jones (1934), remains a magisterial, focused reconstruction of the work of one of the great medieval *scriptoria*. E. A. Lowe's monumental *Codices Latini antiquiores* (1931 ff.) is the sublime culmination of a long lifetime of paleographical artistry. J. M. Manly and Edith Rickert made Chicago the world center of Chaucer studies. Other projects hardly less comprehensive were the work of teams of scholars, usually working at several institutions but guided by a common plan: for example, a study of the English government at work in the early fourteenth century, an edition of the works of Alfonso the Wise of Spain, the source study of the *Roman d'Alexandre* legend in Old French, a new edition of the *Commentary of Servius on Vergil,* Stith Thompson's *Motif Index of Folk Literature* in six volumes, and a new and collaborative history of the Crusades. There were many others of equal range, far too many to list here. Some have fallen by the wayside for various reasons. Many that were barely begun have produced results, either in individual monographs or in articles in learned journals. It is not my task to find the reasons for lack of completion, but certainly the grim reaper, the demotion of scholar to administrator, the heavy teaching load, the impediment of overly demanding students, the discouraging difficulty of access to sources, the weakness of the flesh, the unfortunate limitation of the twenty-four-hour day—these all or singly are our excuse, if we need any.

What is abundantly clear is that as a guild we survived the long war not merely intact, but even improved. Young scholars whose preparation had been interrupted by anywhere from two to five years of military service came back to classes with heightened enthusiasm. It was a great privilege to teach these men—seasoned by travel and matured by the distasteful tasks of destruction and the vestigia of man's hatred for man. To bring such students together to learn about institutions and men, ideas and aspirations, hopes and achievement in another age, distant yet bound to us by our common Western and Christian tradition—this was deeply satisfying. In a long life of teaching, I have never enjoyed any part of the task more than the years immediately following the demobilization of 1946–47. I knew then that the studies of and about the Middle Ages and the Renaissance in America were deeply and firmly rooted and were destined to go from strength to strength. If young scholars who had been through the stresses of war and its dislocations were willing, nay anxious, to rededicate their lives to the *studia spiritualia et humaniora* of a distant age, those studies were in good hands.

But I cannot stop in 1947. Much has happened since then. In these fifteen years, trends only dimly noted have taken on clearer lines. Perhaps the most gratifying development has been a sensible broadening of the coverage. Fields of medieval studies that were barely, if at all, touched before the war of 1939 have since been respectably cultivated, but I shall name only those substantially strengthened in the last fifteen years. Byzantine interests certainly existed in the twenties and thirties, but they were minor and, with some exceptions, amateur. Since then our Byzantinists at Dumbarton Oaks and elsewhere have earned wide recognition and a high place among the leaders in this demanding métier. Several specialized centers have grown up for the study of medieval theology—at St. Bonaventure in New York, the Medieval Institute at Notre Dame, and the Pontifical Institute in Toronto. In the highly specialized area of law, we have made a notable impact. Largely through the the initiative and eminence of one scholar, the Institute for the Study of Canon Law at the Catholic University of America has taken over world leadership in this field. European students are now being sent to Washington to complete their studies in canon law. In Roman and Germanic law, individual American scholars working by themselves have made notable contributions.

In another field, one in which we lagged far behind our European colleagues in the interbellum years—medieval Slavic, especially Western Slavic, studies—we are now vastly improved and on the way to a position of equality. This reversal of relative positions may have some causes other than pure love of recondite learning, but it is nonetheless real. Library facilities are not yet what they should be. Some difficulties remain for those who wish to study in Slavic countries, but they are being surmounted. The quality of the product, both in personnel and in the printed word, is good. It is a growing field; it is also an important field.

The history of medieval science has been recognized since the early twenties, but for many years the recognition was with the guild's left hand. The story of George Sarton's struggles to get any aid or encouragement reads like the trials of Job. Yet he persevered, turning out *Isis* (from 1912 to 1915 in Belgium and afterward in this country) and later *Osiris* almost singlehanded. The concept of the history of science as a separate and valid discipline had difficulty in gaining acceptance. The magnum opus of Lynn Thorndike, the *History of Magic and Experimental Science*, began to appear in 1923 and gave great impetus to the field. The ultimate and hard-won victory of Sarton and Thorndike meant a useful expansion of the whole academic vision. Although almost all the leading universities now offer programs in the history of science, many focusing on the medieval and Renaissance centuries, Sarton, perhaps the most universal in approach of all his contemporaries, was unable to get a steady teaching post in his chosen field for many years. The contrast between 1920 and 1962 is startling.

In another area of specialization, medieval studies in America have moved slowly. Economic history of the Middle Ages did in fact occupy the attention of some American scholars before the end of World War I. Charles Gross, of Harvard, published *The Gild Merchant* in 1890, and English scholars immediately hailed it as a masterpiece of intuition and synthesis. It remains an indispensable classic to this day. Some of his pupils continued to study the economic institutions of England and the Continent, but rather as sidelines than as principal objects of study and research. It is something of an anomaly that in a nation so highly industrialized as ours and in institutions so many of which were founded by the munificence of individuals who had profited from our free economy, more attention has not been given to the study of these very economic forces. At the present moment and for some years in the recent past, it would be my judgment that the most productive and stimulating scholars in America in the field of medieval and Renaissance economic history are foreign born. One is led to wonder whether perhaps the native economist either is afraid of what he might find out about the past of his field or is so concerned with the future that the past is beneath his notice. In either case, some incisive rethinking is in order.

In still another area—the history of art—we can allow ourselves a goodly measure of pride and confidence. America has been blessed by munificent Maecenases who since the middle of the nineteenth century have made notable collections of *objets d'art* and accompanied the collecting with competent interest in the theory and history of art. Institutionally, the discipline grew slowly, but even before the war, at a number of universities and colleges, courses in medieval and Renaissance art were being given. Specifically, traditions for a serious pursuit of art history were well established before 1914, at least at Princeton, Harvard, and New York University. The pioneering work of Allan Marquand at Princeton from the 1880's and of his pupils and successors Frank J. Mather and C. R. Morey was epochal and of amazingly high quality, as was that of Arthur Kingsley Porter at Harvard and his pupil and successor Kenneth J. Conant in Romanesque and early Gothic archeology. The steady growth and spread of these traditions and the work accomplished by American scholars during the last four decades have been remarkable. At the same time, it is only proper to record that some of the scholars now most active in this area are foreign born and still have much to teach us. They have brought depth as well as sensitivity to the whole guild. We are constantly grateful for their contribution. Yet we have good reason to be confident that we can produce their equals from our own soil.

There remain several fields of medieval study in which we may admit that we are late arrivals and at the same time express the hope that we will soon catch up with our European friends. In the area of Byzantine studies, native American masters of the trade are certainly not numerous. Harvard has long been aware of the field, and the untimely death of Robert P. Blake, who was capable of work comparable to that of any European scholar, left a serious lacuna. In this study, there are built-in difficulties for any native-born American. He must command the ancient languages, as well as the modern Romance, Germanic, and Slavic, and perhaps even Turko-Ugric and Arabic tongues. He must be at home in the history and literature of many ages and peoples. An adequate command of a dozen to fifteen languages is not an everyday occurrence among young, or indeed old, American academicians. At present, most of our leading Byzantinists are European born. They have come to their advanced studies with at least half a dozen languages, and they can go on from there to the other sectors of their discipline with relative ease. Yet there are some native-born Byzantinists, and a few more are being turned out. The possibility of combining Byzantine studies with early Slavic or Balkan studies or, on the other hand, with Near Eastern and Arabic studies is beginning to attract hardy students. The market for those competent in this field is improving. I should hazard the guess that at least a dozen young Byzantine Ph.D.'s could be well placed within a very short time—an encouraging development. The fact remains, however, that, over all, we are not well oriented or equipped in Byzantine studies. Apart from Rutgers and Harvard's Dumbarton Oaks, there are no acceptable centers of Byzantine studies in America, but this situation should soon be remedied.

Another field in which our position is promising but as yet inadequate is in the area of medieval Slavdom. Before 1914, some scholars interested in the Slavic world studied in Germany, and German contempt for the Slavic peoples rubbed off on them. The smaller and Western Slavic countries, some with periods of glory and great national achievement during the Middle Ages, were treated with supreme disdain by German scholars. A whole and substantial segment of European culture was thus passed over with a few light remarks about the "peasantry" and "backward tribes." Somebody forgot that both world wars either began or ended in the area of these "peasant" Slavs, whose memories of their medieval past made them impervious to Germanization on the one hand or Russification on the other. Their history has quite naturally made them sensitive to denigration from any source, and as a result their writings about their own past have often been enthusiastic, if not (as is sometimes charged) ultra-nationalistic. Naturally, this tendency needs to be corrected before the results could be accepted by the American reader. Slavic history, medieval or modern, must be written, in the last analysis, by Americans by the name of Smith, Jones, or Brown. In part, this is being done, but thus far only in part. There is as yet no American "school" of medieval Slavic studies, although there are several places where one could arise. Library facilities are steadily and in some cases remarkably improving. Native-born Americans are, in increasing numbers, learning Slavic languages other than Russian. The National Defense Education Act of 1958 has been a powerful economic boon to this field, among others, and the centers for language and area studies set up under its aegis may turn out to be among the most fruitful aids to the equalization of American and European educational preparation that our whole system has known. Medieval Slavic studies have really only just begun in America.

Thus far in this discussion, a broad spectrum of the subdivisions of the discipline of medieval studies in America has been presented, and quite properly so. Each generation of active scholars has passed on its gains to the next. At the end of three-quarters of a century or more, hardly any part of the field has not been worked, often brilliantly, with results that our European colleagues have regarded as, if not definitive, at least solid contributions to the whole corpus.

Once this is said, I think any medievalist would agree with me that it is not enough. We should not be satisfied with what we have done or, indeed, with our present rate of progress. In a number of respects we could properly re-examine our present assumptions and in a few details face up to very obvious and reparable shortcomings.

Medieval studies, whether history, literature, philosophy, art, law, or society, are presented to the student and indeed to the literate public apologetically, almost as if they were an un-American activity. This attitude is fantastic. It overlooks the indisputable fact that we are here dealing with our own past. The Middle Ages are early American history and they should be so presented. From another point of view, the American student has even a better right to interest himself in medieval Europe. All Europe is his *sedes patrum*. For this reason, I suggest that America may hope to produce historians of the European tradition who are unsurpassed in understanding and truthfulness by those of any other land. This we have not yet done. The first step is to realize our responsibility and to raise our sights.

After that, there come technical needs—the tools of the trade. First among them is the control of a number of languages—half a dozen, at least, for scholarly purposes, beginning with the classical languages. It is common for a European medievalist to use ten or a dozen languages. We must accept that standard. The pattern must start early in the grades. Because most of the writings composed during the Middle Ages have not yet been printed, a medievalist, if he is to go to the sources, must be able to read the manuscripts. Latin paleography is taught in regrettably few places in the United States, whereas there is hardly a European university that does not offer courses in paleography and diplomatic. Because of this lack, our young scholars and indeed many of our senior scholars cannot hope to match the depth and solidity of the work of their European contemporaries. This lacuna will have to be filled. It goes without saying that our libraries will have to continue to procure basic titles in this demanding field. Yet our present situation is far from desperate. Interlibrary loans and microreproduction have been of notable help, and much excellent work can be done without leaving our shores. Nothing, however, quite takes the place of direct confrontation of the manuscripts. The feel of the vellum is in itself an education. This means travel. It is a true saying that one never understands the problems of the Habsburg empire until he has tasted Polish borscht, Danubian wines, or Hungarian goulash. Correspondingly, no one has really grasped the meaning of the spirit of Thomas Aquinas until he has held in his hand a few folios of his completely illegible handwriting.

I have no fears on the score of American competence or ultimate achievement in the area of our immediate concern. We have the energy, we have already had very respectable performance, we have built-in perspective, we have more and better scholars coming on, we have the resources to support them, and they will make their own public. We need only patience, wisdom, and a large vision of the importance of these studies to the understanding of our own past and, by implication, to our present relations with our European cousins. Surely this is not too much to expect of a proud and dedicated profession.

LYNN WHITE, JR.

The Medieval Roots of Modern
Technology and Science

To THOSE OF US reared within the enchanted circle of Western civilization, the most treasured part of our tradition is civil rights and their juridical and parliamentary defenses. Since the days of Bishop Stubbs it has been no news that these are to a great extent dividends on the medieval legacy, although subsequent scholarship has greatly amplified and somewhat de-Anglo-Saxonized our view of such matters.

When a Syrian, a Nigerian, or a Burmese looks at the Occident, however, what does he see as really distinctive and valuable? What does he want most eagerly to appropriate for himself and his society? Generally it is not parliamentary democracy, although with the collapse of their own old regimes they have indeed taken over its external forms, *faute de mieux*. What they want are our technology and, secondarily, the natural science that we assure them is fundamental to that technology. The capacity of an industrial society to turn out goods to end the appalling poverty of the non-Western world; its ability to produce the arms that in our mad epoch are the means to a group's self-respect—these, to non-Occidentals, are the hallmarks of Westernization. Russia, beginning with Peter the Great, Japan after the Meiji Restoration, prove to them that democracy is a folkway of the West, whereas technology and science are the essence of its power.

In these papers we are dealing with the newer views of the Middle Ages and of our historical relation with them. Why bring up technol-

LYNN WHITE, JR., is Professor of History at the University of California at Los Angeles. He is a Guggenheim Fellow and a Fellow of the American Academy of Arts and Sciences and the author of *Latin Monasticism in Norman Sicily* and *Medieval Technology and Social Change*. He is a member of the Mediaeval Academy of America and of the History of Science Society. He has been President of the Society for the History of Technology.

ogy and science? It has been axiomatic that the Middle Ages were an Age of Faith, which therefore must have been antipathetic toward anything legitimately called science, and that their technology was both static and negligible. The Scientific Revolution of the seventeenth century and the Industrial Revolution of the eighteenth were the antithesis of everything medieval. "God said 'Let Newton be' and all was light." As for James Watt, it never occurred to the poets that God might have had anything at all to do with him, but this attitude did not seem to reduce his effectiveness. By that time God seemed in any case a bit of a refugee from the shattered Middle Ages.

The axioms, however, are in flux. Now, and for some sixty years past, medieval science has been the subject of increasingly intensive investigation, and during the last two decades we have begun also to have a look at medieval technology, with unexpected results. Much more will be learned, but we are at a point where an intelligible new picture is emerging. What we begin to see is a continuity in the scientific and technological aspects of our culture fully comparable to that long recognized in the legal and constitutional.

Any discussion of continuity and change runs grave risks of setting up false dichotomies. Those who stress change sometimes seem to forget that it takes a river to make a waterfall, as well as a cliff for it to tumble over. Those who tend to dwell on continuity are so entranced by the river that they disregard the cliff. This sort of nonsense can best be avoided if we distinguish between *change* and *discontinuity* in cultural history. Discontinuity occurs when an item or set of items is borrowed from outside a culture and when that borrowing alters the whole style of the relevant activity in the recipient culture. Silver had been mined in Peru and copper in Katanga from very early times. Yet when in the fifteen hundreds the Spaniards brought in Europe's most skilful mining engineers to exploit the treasures of the Andes, and when the Union Minière did the same thing in Central Africa early in our own century, the styles of Andean and Congolese mining suffered such mutations that one must state the events in terms of discontinuity. On the other hand, the engineers who came to Potosí and then to Kolwezi four hundred years later, although their mining methods differed vastly, belonged to the tradition of European mining technology in which there has been much change but no discontinuity. As contrasted with discontinuity caused by borrowed elements, change that is generated internally in a tradition is powerful evidence of the continuity of that tradition.

Until recently the chronology of the Western tradition of technology has been entirely misunderstood. Even in the early Middle Ages, the parts of Europe adhering to the Latin Church began to show a technological dynamism superior to that of the generally more sophisticated cultures of Byzantium and Islam.[1]

Beginning in the sixth century, and accumulating until the end of the ninth century, an interlocking series of innovations led to a revolution in agricultural methods in northern Europe. These were the heavy plow, the open-field system, the triennial rotation of crops, a new type of harness for horses consisting of a rigid collar and lateral traces, and, finally, nailed horseshoes. Some of these may have been borrowed from Central Asia, but on the whole they seem to have been indigenous, as was their integration to form a coherent system of tillage. For climatic reasons, the new agricultural techniques were generally applicable only north of the Loire and the Alps. By the time of Charlemagne, effects of the new productivity of the northern peasants were very noticeable and, indeed, enable us to understand the shift of the focus of Europe away from the Mediterranean's shores to the great plains of the north, where it has remained ever since. By the eleventh century, the unprecedented food surpluses were reflected in a rapid increase of population. Everywhere new cities were springing up and old ones were expanding their walls to defend bursting suburbs. The tempo of manufacture, commerce, and finance accelerated, and a new pattern of urban bourgeois life emerged.

Cultivating the soil has been, until recently, the basic human occupation. We now see that the early Middle Ages produced, in the north, a new kind of agriculture which in terms of human labor was more productive than that of any other civilized society of the time. This illuminates many problems. The stupendous capital expenditure on the Gothic cathedrals, for example, can be understood in the new economic context.

In the technology of warfare, the West likewise seized the initiative as early as the eighth century. During the 730's, there occurred a sharp discontinuity in the history of European warfare, caused by the introduction, from India by way of China, of the stirrup. The stirrup is a curious item in the history of technology because it is both cheap and easy to make, yet it makes a vast difference in what a warrior can do on a horse. As long as a man is clinging to his horse by pressure of his knees, he can wield a spear only with the strength of his arms. But when the lateral support of stirrups is added to the fore-and-aft buttressing of the pommel and cantle of a heavy saddle, horse

[1] Save as is otherwise indicated, detailed support for the following discussion of technology may be found in my *Medieval Technology and Social Change* (Oxford, 1962). The best guide to medieval science remains G. Sarton, *Introduction to the History of Science* (3 vols. in 5; Baltimore, 1927–48) with a careful index.

and rider become one. Now the fighter is enabled—but not required, be it noted—to lay his spear at rest between his upper arm and body. The blow is struck no longer with the strength of a man's muscles but rather by the impetus of a charging stallion and rider. The stirrup thus made possible the substitution of animal power for human power. It was the technological basis for mounted shock combat, the typical Western medieval mode of fighting.

The increase in the violence of attack was immense, and all the peoples in immediate contact with Western Christendom were compelled in self-defense to adopt the new Frankish military technology, for, as the Byzantine princess Anna Comnena ruefully admitted, "a Frank on horseback is invincible."[2] To give just one specific example of this diffusion: By about the year 1000, in order to protect the rider's left leg, the Westerners had elongated the round shield into a kite-shaped shield, pointed at the bottom. By 1066 this is found in Byzantium[3] and by 1085 in Cairo. The Spanish Muslims bitterly lamented that military exigencies had forced them to adopt the lance at rest and the heavy Christian armor and to arm their infantry with the crossbow, which they, like Anna Comnena, regarded as a Frankish novelty designed to pierce the heavy mail made necessary by shock combat.

The medieval West, then, developed not only the most productive agricultural system but also the most effective military technology of the age. The Crusades failed partly because of rivalries between the Westerners, partly because of their difficult logistic problems, but also because the Near East learned European ways of fighting. Nowhere is the admiration of the Muslim military man for the technical methods of his Frankish foes better expressed than in al-Herewī's eyewitness account of the carefully co-ordinated battle tactics, the skilful mutual support by cavalry and infantry, exhibited by the armies of the Third Crusade.

The strangest thing about this whole development is that the Franks were the last horse-riding people of Eurasia to receive the stirrup, yet they were the first to realize and exploit its full implications for warfare. There would seem to have been in the West a greater degree of openness to innovation than was to be found in the more

---

[2] *Alexiad*, trans. E. Dawes (London, 1928), p. 342.

[3] In *Medieval Technology*, p. 35, I dated the Byzantine adoption of the kite-shaped shield *ca.* 1100. For the date 1066, based on British Museum, Cod. add. 19352, fol. 87ᵛ, cf. *Late Classical and Medieval Studies in Honor of Albert Mathias Friend, Jr.*, ed. K. Weitzmann (Princeton, 1955), p. 190, Pl. XXII, 2.

complex and perhaps less turbulent societies of Byzantium, Islam, India, and China of that age.[4]

The most remarkable display of technological adventuresomeness in the medieval West, however, was the elaboration of powered machines and of laborsaving devices in manufacturing. The water mill appeared in the early first century before Christ, but there is as yet no firm evidence that either water or wind power was applied to any industrial process other than grinding grain in antiquity, in Byzantium, or in Islam until very recent times. The Chinese made some progress along this line, but the Near East, like India, seems to have remained very nearly at the Roman level in the utilization of power and labor.

About the year 1000, there is a stirring in the industry of the West. A rudimentary but novel device, cams on the axle of a water wheel, is operating mechanical fulling machines in the textile industry and trip hammers for forging iron. No one has yet screened the available material, eliminating forgeries and tracing diffusions, but when that task is accomplished, our view of European economic history will be profoundly altered. By the late twelfth century, such simple machines were widespread.

The horizontal-axle windmill was invented on the shores of the North Sea shortly after 1180. An earlier vertical-axle windmill is found in southern Afghanistan, perhaps inspired by wind-driven Tibetan prayer cylinders,[5] but it was inefficient and had little diffusion even in Islam. The windmill as we know it is a Western medieval invention which vastly increased power resources in flat lands where the fall of streams was too slight for a good watermill and where a mill dam would flood too much fertile land.

About 1235 another concept emerges. Villard de Honnecourt's notebook shows the sketch of the first industrial machine to involve two correlated, fully automatic motions. It is a water-powered sawmill, which, in addition to the motion of sawing, provides an automatic feed to keep the log pressed against the saw.[6] This reflects the mentality that during the next century produced the incredibly sophisticated automation of the weight-driven mechanical clock, culmi-

[4] I have explored some reasons for this contrast in "What Accelerated Technological Progress in the Western Middle Ages?" in *Scientific Change*, ed. A. C. Crombie, to appear shortly.

[5] See my "Tibet, India and Malaya as Sources of Western Medieval Technology," *American Historical Review*, LXV (1959–60), 515–26.

[6] *The Sketchbook of Villard de Honnecourt*, ed. T. Bowie (Bloomington, Ind., 1959), Pl. 58.

nating in 1364 with the completion of Giovanni Dondi's planetarium at Pavia.[7]

The fourteenth and fifteenth centuries developed further applications of power machinery, notably powered bellows for blast furnaces and a great variety of grinding, polishing, rolling, and wiredrawing devices in the metal industries. By the end of the fifteenth century, the cities of the more industrialized parts of Europe were filled with groups of craftsmen working, it would seem, in relatively small shops; but—in absolute contrast to the Orient—they worked habitually with machines run by natural forces and not merely by human energy.

We must reconsider what we mean by the Industrial Revolution of the eighteenth century. Its essence was not the first discovery of power machinery. Probably the core of it was the emergence of sizable factories. These were made necessary by the fact that, after seven centuries of continuous development, power machinery had reached a point of elaboration, differentiation, and expense that demanded concentration. But, clearly, this is not a historical discontinuity; it is an internally generated managerial innovation.

My fundamental proposition, then, is that the technological dominance of Western culture is not merely characteristic of the modern world: it begins to be evident in the early Middle Ages and is clear by the later Middle Ages.

It has become a platitude that the most important thing about modern technology is not inventions but rather "the invention of invention." There were inventors in antiquity, and among the Greeks in particular there was a considerable—if often mythologizing—interest in the origin of specific innovations. I have not found in antiquity, however, any indication of the idea of invention as a general enterprise looking to the future rather than as the effort to solve a particular problem. The modern notion of invention as a total movement for innovation first finds expression in a famous passage by Roger Bacon, probably written about 1260, in which he anticipates a world of motor ships, automobiles, airplanes, and submarines. Moreover, when we look at the later thirteenth century with its invention of eyeglasses and the emergence of the spinning wheel, with its records of at least two groups of men working to achieve perpetual motion, and an English cleric telling us (1271) how to build a mechanical clock, but admitting that unfortunately not all the bugs had yet been worked out of the machine, we are forced to conclude that Friar Roger was not alone in his vision of planned technical advance.

[7] Giovanni Dondi dall'Orologio, *Tractatus astrarii*, ed. A. Barzon, E. Morpurgo, A. Petrucci, and G. Francescato (Vatican City, 1960).

Indeed, the rapidity with which novelties spread indicates a popular receptivity to anything useful. The navigator's compass coming from China—across Central Asia and not through Islam, it would seem —reached the West at the very end of the twelfth century. By 1218 Jacques de Vitry considered it essential to any sailing on the sea, and seven years later it was already in habitual use in Iceland. Yet no Muslim reference to the compass has been found earlier than 1232–33, which would seem to indicate less receptivity in Islam. An even more spectacular example of speedy diffusion is the windmill. The earliest one firmly dated is found in Yorkshire in 1185, yet seven years later German Crusaders had built the first ever seen in Syria. Within a few decades, it had become a normal part of most European landscapes. When about 1322, an English chronicler can credit the deforestation of England in part to the search for the long beams needed for windmill vanes,[8] we are obviously dealing with an age eagerly exploiting mechanical power.

There is a persistent opinion that before the Industrial Revolution there was widespread opposition to technological changes, particularly on the part of the guilds. The vernacular presentation of this topic cites Suetonius' story of how Vespasian declined to use a laborsaving hoist because it would cause unemployment among the Roman rabble, goes on to the (entirely ineffective) prohibition by the Second Lateran Council in 1139 of the use of the crossbow when fighting fellow Christians, and generally ends with early modern textile workers smashing stocking-knitting machines. We must eventually remedy this sort of rampaging down through the ages. We still lack a firmly constructed history of attitudes toward technological change. As a result of desultory rummagings, I believe at present that in the Middle Ages there was no opposition to any novelty that seemed to those closest to the matter to be profitable. The clergy of the twelfth century might indeed ban the crossbow and two hundred years later might shake benign tonsured pates over the satanic qualities of gunpowder; but the men whose business it was to use weapons used the most effective weapons they could get. The guilds were made up of canny craftsmen interested in efficient production and quite aware that, if they failed to adopt a good new gadget, their export trade would quickly lose markets to the guild in the next city that had permitted its use. Indeed, technological change often caused great disruption of industry yet was not opposed. In a classic study E. M. Carus-Wilson[9] has shown that in thirteenth-century England the dis-

[8] W. Dugdale, *Monasticon anglicanum* (2d ed.; London, 1682), I, 816.

[9] "An Industrial Revolution of the Thirteenth Century," *Economic History Review*, XI (1941), 39–60; cf. *ibid.*, 2d ser., III (1950–51), 342–43.

placement of hand-fulling by mechanical fulling led to the shift of the center of English textile manufacturing from the southeast part of the island to the more accidented northwest, where water-power sites were more readily available. When the spinning wheel first appeared in Europe toward the end of the thirteenth century, it must have caused unemployment among those who provided commercial yarn for the weavers. Yet the first mention of the spinning wheel, in a guild regulation in Speyer, *ca.* 1280, does not forbid it but merely prohibits the use of wheel-spun thread in the warp (as distinct from the weft), presumably because it was not yet as strong as that produced in the old way. The object, then, was to protect the quality of cloth.

It is my impression that very little guild opposition to industrial changes can be found before the sixteenth century and that when at last it appeared it was because the pace of technological advance had become so rapid that a new industrial system was appearing, the guild structure was slipping, and the guilds were fighting for their existence.

Fighting in vain, one must add. The only case in which, as far as I know, a guild succeeded in holding back technical progress for any considerable time was a victory due to entirely exceptional circumstances. In 1534, an Italian, Matteo del Nassaro, built a mill on piles over the Seine at Paris to polish precious stones for jewelry. In 1552 this was bought by the royal mint and equipped with new water-powered machines recently designed at Augsburg to produce coins. In 1563 King Henry II died, and the guild of coiners persuaded the advisers of his sixteen-year-old successor, Francis II, to abandon the enterprise and restrict the use of power machines to the production of medals. Thenceforth in France coins were "struck" in the traditional way until 1645.[10] It is clear, however, that if the guild of coiners had not been dealing with a rigorously enforced royal monopoly of coinage, if they had been in a typical competitive market, their efforts to block innovation would have crumbled quickly, as other such attempts did. As long as the guilds were a flourishing part of medieval society, they were strong enough to accept technological change. Only when the guild structure became senile, because it had lost touch with the new economic order, did the guilds try to block change.

Thus far I have scarcely mentioned medieval science. In the twentieth century, science-and-technology is a hyphenated word, and science has priority in our minds. We think of technology as being applied science.

[10] A. Blanchet and A. Dieudonné, *Manuel de numismatique française* (Paris, 1916), II, 192–93.

The situation in the Middle Ages was entirely different. From what I have said, it is clear that the supremacy of the Occident in technology antedates by several centuries its pre-eminence in science. Moreover, technological achievements and problems cannot be shown to have had much direct influence on the growth of medieval science, and scientific discoveries did not affect the growth of technology.

The history of European technology, from the earliest times to the present, is one of constant change but of no discontinuity as a whole, even at the time of the collapse of the Western Roman Empire. The only striking discontinuity in a single area of technology was that in the art of war in the eighth century brought about by the arrival of the stirrup. Even the development of gunpowder artillery in the early fourteenth century brought no such rapid shift in the style of combat, and in any case cannon may have been indigenous to Europe.

The history of Occidental science, on the other hand, has a much more irregular pattern. There is nothing in the early Western Middle Ages that we would wish to call "science." The Romans were remarkably indifferent to the achievements of Greek science and translated few of the Greek texts into Latin.[11] When knowledge of the Greek tongue decayed in the West, science dropped below its eastern horizon. About the year 1000, Gerbert of Aurillac (Pope Sylvester II), the liveliest scholar of his time in the Latin world, was interested in science and did his best.[12] His actual knowledge of science, however, was pathetic.

The scientific movement in the West, of which we today are the direct heirs, started with a seismic discontinuity in the later eleventh century—a complete break with the past and the borrowing en masse from Byzantium and Islam of ancient Greek science and of the contemporary Arabic science that had been elaborated on Greek and Indic foundations. The suddenness and avidity with which the West turned to an alien science demands explanation, but I shall not attempt it here.[13] Suffice it to say that within about two hundred years, that is, roughly from the first translations of Constantine the African about 1060 to the death of William of Moerbeke in 1286, the great

[11] The excellent study by W. H. Stahl, *Roman Science* (Madison, Wis., 1962), p. 251, asserts that "most of the manifestations of low-level scientific and philosophical thinking that we associate with the Dark Ages appear among the Romans."

[12] One of the earliest indications of versions of Arabic science in Latin appears in Gerbert's letter of 984 to Lupitus of Barcelona asking for an astronomical treatise that the latter had translated; cf. *The Letters of Gerbert*, trans. H. P. Lattin (New York, 1961), p. 69.

[13] For some aspects of the problem, see my "Natural Science and Naturalistic Art in the Middle Ages," *American Historical Review*, LII (1946–47), 421–35.

bulk of Greek and Muslim science was made available in Latin and was rather well assimilated by the West.

From the later thirteenth century onward, Occidentals began making significant original scientific discoveries, as, for example, in Peter of Maricourt's pioneering study (1269) of magnetism. To be sure, the pre-eminence of late medieval science is partly a matter of lack of competition. Byzantium, which in any case had been scholarly rather than experimental in science, was declining under Turkish assault. Islam, after nearly four centuries of brilliant scientific achievements, had begun after 1100 to turn from the study of external facts to the contemplation of the inner fact of the soul,[14] and her scientific vigor waned rapidly. Nevertheless, Western science in the fourteenth and fifteenth centuries has both great inherent interest and high significance for the so-called Scientific Revolution that built upon it.

Late medieval science put little stress on experiment. It was "natural philosophy," highly speculative and often mathematical: for example, early in the fourteenth century, trigonometry spurted ahead in the work of clergy at Merton College, Oxford, and of the Provençal Jew Levi ben Gerson. Both the limitations and the great originality of European science at that time must be understood in the context of the intellectual crises of the period.[15] Conservative theologians were horrified by the implication of Thomas Aquinas' effort to incorporate Aristotelian philosophy into the Christian intellectual system and to make it a rational means of validating what they regarded as revealed truths. To defend their neo-Augustinian position, they launched a savage and brilliant counterattack upon Aristotle, designed to distinguish sharply between the sorts of knowledge that are accessible to human faculties and the sorts of knowledge that can be got only by revelation. In the process, they pushed the whole of metaphysics into the area of revelation. Thus they destroyed the entire prior Greek and Muslim concept of the metaphysical nature of the philosophical venture and invented the empirical, that is, the modern, notion of what philosophy is all about. The crisis of the fourteenth century is thus the most creative moment in the history of Western thought.

It was inherent in the nature of this intellectual revolution that

---

[14] W. Hartner, "Quand et comment s'est arrêté l'essor de la culture scientifique dans l'Islam?" in *Classicisme et declin culturel dans l'histoire de l'Islam*, ed. R. Brunschvig and G. E. von Grunebaum (Paris, 1957), pp. 318–37, should be read in the context of the extraordinary essay by G. E. von Grunebaum, "The World of Islam: The Face of the Antagonist," in *Twelfth-Century Europe and the Foundations of Modern Society*, ed. M. Clagett, G. Post, and R. Reynolds (Madison, Wis., 1961), pp. 189–211.

[15] Best depicted by E. A. Moody, "Empiricism and Metaphysics in Medieval Philosophy," *Philosophical Review*, LXVII (1958), 145–63.

philosophy, which hitherto had been oriented toward theology, should now become reoriented toward science, as it still is. Aristotle's qualitative-metaphysical physics was assaulted by means of a new quantitative-empirical physics. By daring and ingenious analysis, for example, it was shown that Aristotle's theory of moving bodies was false, and a new theory of motion was propounded which is essentially that of Galileo or Newton.[16]

Unfortunately, the scholastic scientists thought that if they had proved a point logically, they had proved it. Some generations passed before it was widely felt necessary to supplement pure thought by rolling balls down inclined planes or dropping weights from towers and timing the fall. The Scientific Revolution of the seventeenth century was in every sense the child of late medieval science, although a rebellious child. There grew up discontent with speculative science, a realization of the necessity for experiment, and an instinct for the working hypothesis as a guide to experiment. Here we observe great change, but no discontinuity.

There is, however, another significant element in the build-up for the age of Kepler, Descartes, and Newton: the successes of medieval technology. I have not found any instance during the Middle Ages of a scientific discovery that resulted in technological innovation. Indeed, I doubt whether any such case can be established before Von Guericke's and Papin's investigation of vacua and pressures clarified the problem of harnessing steam power. There is, however, a flow of ideas and stimuli from technology to science in the earlier period.

In one medieval case, a scientific *need*, not a discovery, resulted in technological advance. Astronomers found water clocks unsatisfactory because on cold nights the outlets became coated with ice and the timing of observations was inaccurate. Mercury could be substituted for water, but it was costly. Sand abraded the aperture through which it flowed, and in any case there is no sign of a sandglass much earlier than the mechanical clock. Obviously, a weight-driven clock was needed. For perhaps seventy years, astronomers and mechanics struggled to devise one. At last, shortly before the 1340's, they succeeded, and within a few decades Europe was filled with mechanical clocks of astonishing elaboration. The building and repair of them and the rapid emergence of a large clock- and watch-making industry established the basis for providing the exact mechanical apparatus of subsequent scientific investigation. The greatest single need at the present time in the history of science is a rigorous and detailed history of

---

[16] For the continuity of the discussion of motion between the fourteenth and the seventeenth centuries, see M. Clagett, *The Science of Mechanics in the Middle Ages* (Madison, Wis., 1959), pp. 629-71.

instrumentation.[17] It would show, I suspect, that lags in science have often been related to a dearth of technical means for securing information and that scientific advance has often attended a technological breakthrough.

Such a study might also explain puzzling delays in the development of scientific apparatus long after craftsmen had made their elements available. In the Museum of the History of Science in Florence, one may view Galileo's telescope, which transformed Copernicus' mathematical-speculative, late medieval astronomical system into modern observational Copernicanism. One genuflects before the memory of Galileo; but then one wonders why that telescope had not been invented three centuries earlier.

Certainly if someone like John Buridan had used a telescope, we could not be astonished. By the fourteenth century, the study of theoretical optics had reached a remarkable state, providing, for example, sophisticated explanations of the rainbow. Moreover, in the thirteenth century, lenses and their magnifying properties came to be known. Fra Salimbene tells us that when the relics of St. Mary Magdalene were found in Provence in 1283 a parchment was found with them which "vix potuit legi . . . cum cristallo propter scripture antiquitatem."[18] A friend of Bacon made a lens with great effort, which Bacon sent as a gift to the pope. Moreover, Bacon knew, as did Robert Grosseteste, that lenses placed in a series increase magnification. Doubtless the earliest thirteenth-century lenses were made of rock crystal, but toward the end of the century, the Italian glass industry learned how to produce a clear and colorless glass like crystal.[19] At that same moment, methods of cutting rock crystal and gems were greatly improved,[20] and these advances assisted the grinding of good lenses from glass as well. In the late 1280's, a man who lived along the lower Arno, probably in Pisa or Lucca, invented eyeglasses. We do not know his name, but there is an explicit and convincing reference to him in a sermon preached in Florence a few years later.[21] In Europe

[17] A. Rohde, *Die Geschichte der wissenschaftliche Instrumente vom Beginn der Renaissance bis zum Ausgang des 18. Jahrhunderts* (Leipzig, 1923), and G. Boffito, *Gli strumenti della scienza e la scienza degli strumenti* (Florence, 1929), are outdated. M. Daumas, *Les instruments scientifiques aux XVIIe et XVIIIe siècles* (Paris, 1953) is excellent for the period covered.

[18] *Cronica*, ed. O. Holder-Egger (Hanover, 1905–13), p. 520.

[19] A. Gasparetto, *Il vetro di Murano* (Venice, 1958), pp. 59–61.

[20] H. R. Hahnloser, "Scola et artes cristellariorum de Veneciis, 1284–1319," in *Venezia e l'Europa, Atti del XVIII Congresso Internazionale di Storia dell'Arte* (Venice, 1956), pp. 157–65.

[21] E. Rosen, "The Invention of Eyeglasses," *Journal of the History of Medicine and Allied Sciences*, XI (1956), 13–46.

the use of eyeglasses quickly became normal; thence they spread over Eurasia: about 1480 the Persian poet Jāmī still speaks of eyeglasses as "Frankish."[22]

In these circumstances, why didn't the fourteenth century have the telescope? I do not know. All that can be said at present is that when at last a contemporary of Galileo did achieve it, he was resting his invention on the work of late-thirteenth-century glass-makers and gem-cutters.

Instrumentation, then, was one of the ways in which medieval technology aided the scientific movement. In another way, technology gave scientists new problems to think about. As we have seen, the mariner's compass was a novelty in the thirteenth century. Peter of Maricourt's *Epistola de magnete* would seem to have been inspired by watching compass-makers at work, possibly at the port of Amalfi, because we know that he wrote it to relieve boredom at the lengthy siege of Lucera in 1269, where he was serving Charles of Anjou as a military engineer. His treatise is today recognized as the cornerstone of William Gilbert's *De magnete* (1600) and therefore of our entire knowledge of magnetism.

Another stimulus to science came from ballistics. It has often been pointed out that Galileo was intensely interested in the activities at the arsenal of Venice, and some have gone so far as to assert that seventeenth-century physics was born of such technological concerns. This is an oversimplification, because it disregards the continuity of early modern physics with that of the fourteenth century. Late medieval physicists were entirely conscious that the projectiles of trebuchets and cannon involved the theory of moving bodies, and they occasionally refer to them. The seventeenth-century emphasis on the importance of observation and experiment simply brought physics closer to the phenomena provided by artillery, to the eventual advance of both science and technology.

One of my students, Sheldon Shapiro, has recently turned up a particularly elegant and clear case in which a mechanical device posed to science a basic theoretical problem. He has pointed out for the first time that the suction pump was invented in Italy somewhat before the middle of the fifteenth century. The suction pump enabled Galileo to observe that a column of water breaks at about thirty-two feet, and it is difficult to imagine other circumstances, save the siphon, in which anyone could have noticed this phenomenon. I need not elaborate here the vast implications of the study of vacua and atmospheric pressures that eventuated.

---

[22] A. J. Arberry, *Classical Persian Literature* (London, 1958), p. 440. I owe this reference to my colleague Gustave von Grunebaum.

During the Middle Ages, then, and indeed into the seventeenth century, insofar as science and technology were related, influences passed from technology to science much more powerfully than from science to technology. When does the direction of flow change and the modern dependence of technology upon scientific discovery develop? In industrial chemistry, there are signs of it at the end of the eighteenth century, but one must recall that Pasteur's greatest insights stemmed from technical problems like those of the brewing industry. The industrial laboratory with any initial concern for basic scientific discoveries that it is hoped may possibly have application is a creation of the early twentieth century. If one regards this change in the connection between science and technology as the primary event of modern history, then the Middle Ages extend to the death of the Good Queen, the Albert Memorial becomes authentic Gothic, and Rudyard Kipling is the last of the Crusaders—a tenable hypothesis!

The essential relationship between science and technology in the Middle Ages, however, may be deeper than any we have mentioned. The agricultural revolution of the early Middle Ages made possible rapid urbanization. The new bourgeois groups quickly applied water- and wind-power to production. The result was a prosperous, adventurous Europe, much interested in physical and earthly matters and firmly convinced of the Christian doctrine that the world was created for man's benefit and that he has a spiritual responsibility to master it. Medieval technology was therefore instrumental in evoking and supporting a society with attitudes congenial to the effort to understand natural phenomena. The feverish appropriation of Greek and Arabic science from the eleventh through the thirteenth centuries can best be understood in such terms.

Let me add a coda. Thus far I have not used the word "Renaissance." In the history of literature, the fine arts, and philosophy—at least the history of the Platonic philosophy, which for a time attempted to revive metaphysics—the concept of a classical Renaissance starting in Italy and spreading in widening circles appears to be indispensable. It may have some validity also for political theory, but for the history of practical politics, economics, and social change it seems irrelevant, save as individuals and groups strove to find status by embellishing themselves with classical ornament. In the history of science and technology, I do not find the idea of a Renaissance useful for interpreting the facts.

As is now recognized, the chief period of Europe's reappropriation of Greek science extends from the later eleventh century through the thirteenth century and marks the birth of our present scientific movement. During the later fifteenth and the sixteenth centuries, the revival of Greek studies in the West led to the recovery of some Greek scientific writings that had escaped medieval translation and to the editing of the far larger mass of Greek texts that had long been known in translations of varying merit. The scholarly interest of such publication was great, but what was the scientific increment of all this philological activity? Historians, just because their trade leads them to enjoy original texts carefully edited, have generally been deceived in this matter. The most significant of the works newly recovered in the sixteenth century were those of Archimedes, the substance of which had been only partly known through later Greek and Arabic treatises. The new Archimedes greatly stimulated both mathematics and physics. The fact that it was published in 1543, the year that likewise saw the appearance of Copernicus' work and of Vesalius' *Fabrica*, indicates, however, that it was in no way decisive for the European scientific movement. By the later fifteenth and sixteenth centuries—a period when for the first time the West was dazzled by the vision of Greek poetry, drama, history, and art—Europe's science had relatively little to learn from antiquity: five centuries of assimilation were reaching the end of their work.

The case is even clearer in technology. Vitruvius was not widely read in the Middle Ages because the men who built Cluny and Beauvais did not need him. He had tremendous vogue in the Renaissance not for his engineering but for his esthetics: he enabled architects to recover the canons of the Roman style and helped to validate the revolt against the Gothic.

In the sixteenth century, Hero of Alexandria's works were recovered and edited. The Western Middle Ages had not translated them, any more than they had Latinized al-Jarazi's Arabic book on automata (A.D. 1205), which in Islam was so highly regarded that it went into Persian and (probably) Turkish versions. The reason would seem to be that by the thirteenth century Western technicians were already exploring more advanced mechanical forms of automation than are found in the Hellenistic and Muslim treatises. The cock, crowing and flapping its wings, that by 1354 was crowning the great clock of Strasbourg was structurally much more complex than anything described in the classical or oriental works. Even after the publication of Hero's writings, the automata of the later Renaissance and Baroque generally followed the medieval mechanical tradition rather than the hydraulic and pneumatic precedents of earlier technologies.

During the fifteenth and sixteenth centuries, Italy, and to a slightly less extent the north as well, was seething with technological innovation. I have examined several of the still unpublished manuscripts of engineers of this period and find in them an excitement, an originality, and a significance for the origins of the modern world that make them as fascinating as anything that contemporary art or literature can offer. But, whereas the architectural sketches in these notebooks are invariably classicizing, I see no trace in them of recovered items of ancient engineering, save the hodometer, nor can I suggest what else of use there was to have been recovered. The classical Renaissance, which in some areas of life was an inundating wave, created scarcely a ripple in technology. Despite many incidental borrowings, especially from China, the technological tradition of the Occident, which achieved its dynamism in the early Middle Ages, has been subject to few strong external influences. It has moved under its own impetus of creativity from its origins to our own day.

A. C. CROMBIE

The Relevance of the Middle Ages
to the Scientific Movement

IN THE FIRST VOLUME of his *Science and Civilisation in China*, Joseph Needham asks the question: "Why . . . did *modern* science, the tradition of Galileo, Harvey, Vesalius, Gesner, Newton, universally verifiable and commanding universal rational assent . . . develop round the shores of the Mediterranean and the Atlantic, and not in China or any other part of Asia?"[1] "China," he writes, "produced no Aristotle";[2] and no Euclid or Bacon or Descartes. Why?

The year before the publication of Dr. Needham's first volume, the same question put in a letter to a well-known scientist elicited the now famous reply:

Dear Sir, The development of Western Science has been based on two great achievements, the invention of the formal logical system (in Euclidean geometry) by the Greek philosophers, and the discovery of the possibility of finding out causal relationships by systematic experiment (Renaissance). In my opinion one need not be astonished that the Chinese sages have not made these steps. The astonishing thing is that these discoveries were made at all. Sincerely yours, A. Einstein.[3]

ALISTAIR CAMERON CROMBIE is Senior Lecturer in History of Science at Oxford. He is a graduate of Melbourne University and of Cambridge University and originally taught and did research in the field of biology. Since 1946 he has concentrated on the history and philosophy of science, and he has published extensively in this field. He is the author of *Augustine to Galileo: The History of Science A.D. 400–1650* (London, 1952; 2d ed., 2 vols., *Medieval and Early Modern Science*, New York, 1959), of *Robert Grosseteste and the Origins of Experimental Science, 1100–1700* (Oxford, 1953), and of numerous articles in learned journals. He is now joint editor of *History of Science*, an annual review of the literature, research, and teaching in the subject.

1 Joseph Needham, *Science and Civilisation in China* (Cambridge, 1954), I, 19.

2 *Ibid.*, p. 18.

3 See D. J. de S. Price, *Science since Babylon* (New Haven, Conn., 1961), p. 15, n. 10.

The historical problems raised both by the origins of modern scientific thinking in the West and by the existence in the old civilizations of the East of corresponding scientific origins that somehow failed to develop have a topical interest for us now as we watch the appropriation, at ever increasing pace, of Western science by the modern peoples of Asia and Africa. Modern science itself began by an earlier act of appropriation of Aristotelian and Euclidean Greek science and of Arabic science by the peoples of Western Europe whose culture was based on the Latin language. The history of the scientific movement both in antiquity and in medieval and modern times shows natural science to be, not simply part of the natural heritage of mankind (whatever that would mean), but an invention of intellectual art, transmitted by cultural diffusion.

I shall take as the central theme for this paper an examination of the consequences of this medieval act of appropriation in generating the second great achievement indicated by Einstein, the methods by which cogent experimentation was introduced into scientific argument. But I shall also try to show that its topicality and relevance for us extend far beyond this austerely scientific achievement. Together with rational experimental science were generated intellectual attitudes still characteristic of the West. And the appropriation of the superior Arabic and Byzantine intellectual cultures by the barbarous peoples of the medieval Latin West offers a case history with many parallels today in the mental and social transformations brought about by the invasion by Western science and technology, and by their accompanying philosophy of secular reason, of societies guided until recently largely by religion and custom.

From the parochial point of view of modern historical scholarship, the study of the origins of modern science has suffered some very curious consequences from coming last in the studies of the historical movements that are held to have made modern Western civilization. It is a commonplace among the sophisticated that the terms "Renaissance," "Reformation," and "Scientific Revolution" refer to purely conventional divisions of periods and must not be given any causal or even descriptive significance. Yet it seems that this critical sophistication does not always go very deep, for there is still much history being written as if the advent of effective science was one of a succession of stages in a single movement of the liberation of the European intellect from whatever is held to have bound it—ignorance, dogma, custom, superstition. . . . When we recall the origin of this periodization itself, the apparent difficulty of being liberated from *it* becomes understandable. It is the cumulative product of a series of historical judgments made at different times and in differing circumstances in order to define a position in relation to the immediate past with a view to contemporary action. The picture presented of the past became an essential element in a formula of reform being offered as necessary for present and future progress.

As everyone knows, the concept of a renaissance was developed in the fifteenth century itself by admirers of the republican political virtues of ancient Rome, of Cicero's Latin style, and of the naturalistic ideal of ancient sculpture and painting, all of which they saw being revived in Italy and especially in Florence. By the end of the fifteenth century, the humanist historians had established the standard division of European history into antiquity, a period of barbarism for which Nicholas of Cusa coined the term "middle age,"[4] and a recent revival for which the term *la rinascita* was first used by the art historian Vasari.[5] To these already different political, literary, and artistic elements in this concept of a renaissance, a fourth was added in the sixteenth century: Erasmus' conception of a close causal connection between the revival of learning and that of religion.[6] Science was brought into the concept in the seventeenth century, first by such reformers of philosophy as Francis Bacon and Descartes, who used their picture of past stagnation as a means of promoting their new experimental and mathematical methods, and second by such writers as George Hakewill,[7] William Wotton,[8] and Fontenelle,[9] who produced the recent scientific successes as the trump card with which they completed the triumph of the Moderns over the Ancients and replaced a past classical ideal with a vision of future progress as the goal for action.

As a framework into which to fit an account of the origins of modern science, the obvious disadvantage of this historical scheme has come from its linking of these different events in politics, literature, art, religion, and science causally in a single series. The linkage between the revival of classical learning, the Protestant Reformation, and the liberation of the intellect to pursue scientific inquiry can be found, for example, in Bayle's *Dictionary* and in the writings of the

[4] Sir George Clark, *Early Modern Europe from about 1460 to about 1720* (Oxford, 1957), p. 19.

[5] Wallace K. Ferguson, *The Renaissance in Historical Thought* (Cambridge, Mass., 1949), pp. 59–67.

[6] *Ibid.,* p. 54.

[7] *An Apologie or Declaration of the Power and Providence of God in the Government of the World* (Oxford, 1635).

[8] *Reflections upon Ancient and Modern Learning* (London, 1964).

[9] *Entretiens sur la pluralité des mondes: Digressions sur les anciens et les modernes,* ed. R. Shackleton (Oxford, 1955).

American author Cotton Mather.[10] Voltaire used it for his own
sophisticated purposes as a stick with which to beat those whom he
saw as the enemies of enlightenment in his time. The disadvantage of
allowing it to survive any longer in our time is that it is a framework
that can no longer accommodate the known facts.

The two important facts established by the scholarship of the last
seventy or eighty years are, first, that the period during which the
Latin West reappropriated the scientific thought of antiquity came
before the humanist literary revival. From early in the twelfth century, Western scholars sought out and translated into Latin the scientific and philosophical learning in Greek and Arabic as eagerly as any
humanist scholar, with the difference that they were primarily interested in scientific and philosophical writings for their content and not
in literary and historical writings for their style. They traveled like
Adelard of Bath to Sicily and Syria, they worked in places recovered
from Islam like Gerard of Cremona in Toledo, or like William of
Moerbeke they went to Greece. By the end of the thirteenth century
they had made available in Latin the bulk of the Greek science that has
come down to us, and had met and mastered the challenge of the superior Arabic learning of the intellectual and political enemy who occupied the southern shore of the Mediterranean. The later, humanist
contribution to knowledge of ancient science was to produce better
editions and translations. Nor does the view survive inspection that
the medieval scholars merely accepted these new authorities. "We of
later ages should supply what the ancients lacked," Roger Bacon
wrote, "since we have entered into their labours. And by these, unless
we are asses, we can be aroused to better things, because it is most
miserable always to use old discoveries and never to be on the track
of new ones. Christians should . . . complete the paths of the unbeliev-
ing philosophers, not only because we are of a later age and should
add to their works, but so that we may also bend their labours to our
own ends."[11]

The second fact that our account of the origins of modern science
must accommodate is the more or less continuous technological progress observable in the West, beginning in the period of the invasions
and proceeding throughout the Middle Ages in broad independence
of political and cultural events, apart from some specific connections
with science scarcely in evidence before the thirteenth century. Polit-

[10] *American Tears upon the Ruines of Greek Churches* (Boston, Mass., 1701);
see A. C. Crombie, "Historians and the Scientific Revolution," *Endeavour,* XIX
(1960), 9–13.

[11] *The "Opus Majus" of Roger Bacon,* ed. J. H. Bridges (Oxford, 1897), I, 57.
For the medieval view of Islam, see N. Daniel, *Islam and the West: The Making of
an Image* (Edinburgh, 1960).

ical and cultural periodization is largely irrelevant for technology, yet medieval technology laid foundations for all subsequent technology and for science in several important ways. It developed power machinery based on water-, wind-, and ox- or horse-driven mills and such automatically self-adjusting machinery as the mechanical clock. It was inventive and active in applying inventions as shown by the clock, the compass, cartography, spectacles. It made a strong move toward precision, as in metallurgical assaying and in astronomical and mathematical instruments and computers, which provided the prototypes for scientific instrumentation.

That these facts of scientific and technological history should prove impossible to accommodate in a historical scheme designed by political and cultural historians in ignorance of them—or at least ignoring them—should not surprise us. What concerns me is that an a priori acceptance of the scheme should make the facts indigestible to historians who know them well. Let me give an example from an essay by an eminent medievalist published in 1951 and entitled "Why Was Science Backward in the Middle Ages?" His argument is distinguished by a fearless drawing of the conclusion from a major and a minor premise standing in apparent contradiction. After giving a sketch of medieval scientific and technological achievements, he concludes as follows:

In this way the very achievement of the late twelfth and thirteenth centuries merely underlines the verdict about the Middle Ages as a whole. The men of the Middle Ages were unable to do more than they did because they were lacking in scientific incentive. What they achieved in advancing the practical arts of humanity or in preserving and transmitting ancient learning, they did in so far and as long as they were not typically medieval.

In syllogistic form the argument runs:

Major premise a priori: There was no medieval science.
Minor premise from evidence: But there was medieval science.
Conclusion: Therefore medieval science was not medieval.
The premises could yield an alternative conclusion:
Therefore medieval science was not science.

This alternative was chosen by another medievalist in 1961. But I want to draw another conclusion altogether: that the time has come to forget this historical scheme supplying this nonsensical major premise and to look again at the facts.

To understand the development of scientific thought in the Middle Ages or in any other period we do indeed need to consider its linkage with the intellectual and social motives and opportunities that may have stimulated it in certain directions and blocked it in others. I shall devote the rest of this paper to a brief examination of some of the effects of the internal intellectual needs and external social pressures acting on scientific thinking in the Middle Ages in relation to three questions:

(1) scientific cosmology in face of theology;
(2) *scientia experimentalis* as a method of inquiry;
(3) quantification in science and in technology.

In each case I shall also consider the relevance of the medieval position to later developments of the scientific movement. I shall aim to illustrate the thesis that we must look in the later medieval West for the origins of certain essential methods of inquiry and of habits and attitudes of mind characteristic of the modern scientific movement, even when these were based on motives and conceptions of nature that we no longer accept.

(1) *Scientific cosmology in face of theology.* The encounter between what we may call the cosmologies of reason and of revelation in the thirteenth and fourteenth centuries is one of the most interesting episodes in Western intellectual history. It led to positions being taken up that have been formally repeated again and again when there has been a similar conflict between doctrines and intellectual loyalties derived from different sources. In Christian thinking, the first such encounter was that between pagan philosophy and Christian belief in late classical times, and the broad intellectual policy to be followed by medieval Christian philosophers was that laid down by St. Augustine in *De Genesi ad litteram.* Beginning with the basic principle that truth is self-consistent, St. Augustine had ruled out a priori any real contradiction between the data of divine revelation, true by definition in the light of their source, and the equally true data of observation and conclusions of valid reasoning. Any apparent contradiction must arise, he said, out of our incomplete understanding of the true meanings of the conflicting statements and would be resolved when these were correctly interpreted in the light of their different purposes. The Hebrew Scriptures expounding spiritual and moral doctrine need not necessarily be taken literally when they referred to a flat earth and a domed sky, in contrast to the globe and spheres of the Greek astronomers. The way was similarly opened for recognizing that expositions of physical and philosophical doctrines need not all be taken literally either. But a possibility of conflict remained, depending on the amount of irreducible core insisted upon on each side. The intellectual positions taken up when this debate arose once more in the thirteenth century were to be repeated in the controversy over the Copernican sys-

tem in which Galileo found himself engaged and again in that over Genesis and geology and evolution in the nineteenth century. They were paralleled also in the debates provoked by the use of Nature as a guide to human morality by nineteenth-century Romantic political philosophers and Darwinian sociologists, in the intellectual situation created by the Soviet concept of a Marxist science, and in some respects in the history of twentieth-century positivism.

In the thirteenth century the primary encounter was not directly of theological doctrine based on revelation with natural science as such, but with rational philosophical doctrines with which some scientific doctrines were associated. Purely technical science had no part in the encounter at all. Indeed, in the twelfth century, philosophical theologians had used their new learning to follow St. Augustine's advice and offer a rational exegesis of Scripture, as Thierry of Chartres used Plato's *Timaeus* to give a rational account of the days of creation described in Genesis. The conflict arose over specific metaphysical doctrines contained in Latin translations of Aristotle's philosophical writings and of Arabic exegeses of them, especially by Avicenna and by Averroës, which went into circulation in the early thirteenth century. The Western response to these texts was, first, local prohibitions against their use in teaching institutions and then, that failing, the taking-up of intellectual positions. I am concerned only with the effect of this encounter on philosophy of science. We can see this best by looking at some of the effects on one science—astronomy—of positions taken up in relation to one philosophical doctrine: that the universe is not a creation in time of God's free will but an eternal emanation of his intellect, and that it is possible for the human reason to know that intellect in such a way as to discover not only how the world is constituted but why it must necessarily be so constituted and not otherwise.

According to Averroës' followers in the thirteenth century, Aristotle had long ago discovered this necessary constitution of the universe. In *De Caelo* (ii. 3), Aristotle himself had in fact argued in a brilliant tour de force that the cosmology he described was the only possible system that could follow from God's known essence. This required that the heavens, aspiring to imitate God's eternal activity, should move uniformly in a circle; this in turn required the existence of earth at rest at the center; and so on. We have evidence of the use of this argument by Averroïsts in the list of propositions recorded in the *Chartularium Universitatis Parisiensis*[12] as having been condemned by the Bishop of Paris, Stephen Tempier, in 1277. These include:

[12] *Chartularium Universitatis Parisiensis*, ed. H. Denifle and A. Chatelain (Paris, 1889), pp. 546–49.

"Quod Deus non possit movere celum motu recto. Et ratio est, quia tunc relinqueret vacuum" (49). "Quod Deus non potest irregulariter, id est, alio modo, quam movet, movere aliquid, quia in eo non est diversitatis voluntatis" (50). "Quod theologi dicentes quod celum quandoque quiescit, arguunt ex falsa suppositione; et, quod dicere, celum esse, et non moveri, est dicere contradictoria" (100). The example of Paris was followed in the same year by the Archbishop of Canterbury, John Pecham, author of a popular textbook on optics. The theologians condemned these propositions in order to affirm God's absolute, omnipotent freedom. The effect on natural philosophers was that they felt free to explore in scholastic exercises the consequences of God's having created the universe according to various hypothetical possibilities, for example, with the earth in motion instead of the heavens, or with infinite space containing several worlds like our own.

Astronomy at this time was already in purely scientific difficulties. There were in existence three different mathematical systems: the concentric spheres of Eudoxus, whose operation Aristotle had explained physically but which were known not to fit the facts, and Ptolemy's two systems of epicycles and eccentrics, which fitted the facts but were inexplicable by any system of physics. The interest of the moves now made in the search for the true system of astronomy is that they involved two different types of argument that were to reappear again in the Copernican debates and are indeed involved in some form in almost every search for scientific explanation.

The first move was to throw all existing systems open to doubt by the use of the argument that any attempt to infer a cause from an effect involves the logical fallacy of affirming the consequent in a conditional proposition. For example, "if p (epicycles) then q (observed motions of planets), but q therefore p" is logically invalid unless we know that the effect can have come about in only one possible way. But how can we be sure of this unique cause? This situation was pointed out by Thomas Aquinas for mathematical theories in astronomy and was to be used again by Osiander in his preface to Copernicus' *De Revolutionibus*, by Cardinal Bellarmine against Galileo, by Francis Bacon, and as an act of prudence (after Galileo's condemnation) by Descartes, to argue that all such theories are simply convenient calculating devices.[13] They were all equally disqualified from giving a true account of the world. The theological motive during the Copernican debate was, of course, to save Scripture from

[13] The best survey of these arguments is still Pierre Duhem's "Essai sur la notion de théorie physique de Platon à Galilée," *Annales de philosophie chrétienne*, 4th ser., VI (1908).

contradiction by science. A theological motive can also be seen in the subtle and powerful arguments by which William of Ockham denied the possibility of any rational knowledge of the world and reduced the order of natural events to an order of fact, depending on God's inscrutable will, which science can simply organize in convenient ways. The theological origins of positivism would repay further investigation by historians of philosophy. For astronomy, arguments of this type loosened the bonds of existing theories, but, by making the choice between rival theories of equal accuracy simply one of convenience, they did little to help the positive search for something better.

The positive advances in astronomical theory were made by an altogether different argument, making range of application the main distinguishing criterion of a true theory. I do not know of anyone before Kepler[14] who explicitly shrugged off the fallacy of affirming the consequent as simply part of all inductive scientific reasoning and offered this different criterion as the serious one, but this policy had in effect been stated in antiquity by Geminus in asserting that the choice between rival mathematical theories in astronomy must be made by physics. Ptolemy had tried to make the geostatic assumptions of his system plausible by empirical and physical arguments. In the fourteenth century Jean Buridan introduced in his theory of impetus a dynamical explanation of the motion both of projectiles and falling bodies and of the celestial spheres. Here was the beginning of a single physical criterion for distinguishing between theories requiring possible and impossible motions over the entire range of moving bodies, terrestrial and celestial.

Later in the fourteenth century Nichole Oresme, in his French commentary on Aristotle's *De Caelo* commissioned by Charles V of France, used a modified version of the impetus theory to argue that, Aristotle notwithstanding, the daily rotation of the earth on its axis was a possible motion. He argued that mathematical astronomy based on this assumption would be able to account for all the phenomena much more economically than on the geostatic assumption. Hence, since "God and Nature do nothing in vain,"[15] it would be reasonable to assume that God had in fact created the universe with the earth and not the spheres in motion. He systematically met the observational and physical objections to the earth's rotation by arguments that Copernicus was to parallel closely two centuries later. In reply to the

14 Kepler's arguments will be discussed in a forthcoming study of his *Apologia Tychonis* by my colleagues H. R. Harré and T. Beardsworth.

15 *Le livre du ciel et du monde* (Book II, chap. xxv), ed. A. D. Menut and A. S. Denomy, *Medieval Studies*, III–V (1941–43), 278.

objection that it was the heavens that appear to rotate, he pointed out that all motion as observed is relative; and against Aristotle's physical requirement of a static earth as the unique gravitational center of the universe, he argued that gravity, spatial directions, and motion are all relative only to each particular world among all the possible worlds that God may have created in infinite space. Following St. Augustine's methods, Oresme also met objections from such biblical texts as that describing Joshua's miracle, implying that the heavens are in motion and the earth at rest, by pointing out that Scripture simply "conforms in this part to the manner of common human speech."[16]

In the end, Oresme recognized that his arguments had not positively proved the earth's rotation but had simply shown that the contrary had not been proved either. So he accepted the text, "Deus enim firmavit orbem terrae, qui non commovebitur" (Vulgate, Psalm 92), as the literal truth and treated his whole argument as an intellectual exercise. Yet it was a repetition of the same exercise in the seventeenth century that was to provide Newton with his decisive criterion. Within the system of classical mechanics, confirmed over the whole tested range of moving bodies, only some motions are possible, and these do not include those required by a geostatic system. So Newton distinguished the true system of astronomy as that which treated a planet as a projectile moving in one of a family of conic sections and made the earth a sputnik in orbit round the sun.

While range of application has become established as the most powerful criterion for choosing the most acceptable theories, the other arguments used in these medieval discussions have also left their mark on scientific thinking. Both the theological argument that the universe is a contingent product of God's free will, and the logical argument that all inference from effects to unique causes involves a logical fallacy, make knowledge of ultimate causes of the type envisaged by Aristotle effectively unattainable. Aquinas had drawn a distinction between two ways of establishing theoretical principles. In one, "sufficient reason could be brought to prove the principle,"[17] and he gave as an example the uniformity of the heavenly movements. "In the other way, reasons may be adduced which do not sufficiently prove the principle, but which may show that the effects which follow agree with it." He gave as an example the eccentric and epicycle systems and pointed out that the fallacy of affirming the consequent makes the proof insufficient. This same distinction was to be made again by Newton, Huygens, and other scientific thinkers in the seventeenth century and again many times since. The difference

[16] *Ibid.*, p. 276.
[17] *Summa theologica*, Part I, q. 32, art. 1.

is that Newton and Huygens saw clearly that the "sufficient reason" for accepting a principle was not to be drawn from some principle of ontological "fitness" such as Aquinas used, but from a theory of wider application, as Newtonian dynamics gave sufficient reason for accepting Kepler's elliptical planetary orbits. So these distinct types of argument used in medieval astronomy have in combination very powerfully helped to clarify what is meant by a true theory in science.

(2) Scientia experimentalis *as a method of inquiry.* In all scientific inquiry there are two distinct elements: a concept of the nature of the world being investigated, and methods of carrying out the investigation. In any growing science these two elements continually interact with each other, and the methods of inquiry may eventually help to create an entirely new conception of the world. I shall discuss now some of the types of argument and method used by academic natural philosophers in the thirteenth and fourteenth centuries. I want to emphasize the need, in trying to understand early science, to pay attention to the arguments and methods as such, even when the conception of the world with which they were associated is one we no longer accept. We should also remember the circumstances in which scientific inquiries were carried out in the medieval universities and religious teaching orders. These institutions performed a function, without parallel on the same scale in antiquity, in providing for continuity of knowledge from one generation to the next so that a genuine philosophical community with generally accepted aims, methods, and standards could come into being. This medieval philosophical community has survived in the professional scientific community of our own times. The surprising historical phenomenon—surprising anyhow in the view of history I discussed in my introduction—may seem to be that a community of scholars whose normal method of working was commenting on Aristotle and other standard texts should have been interested in original scientific inquiry at all. Even more interesting as a historical problem is to find at the heart of this medieval academic culture, aiming primarily to train servants of church and state, both an intense interest in the logic of experimental science and a few experimental inquiries actually carried out.

Any attempt to estimate the meaning of the medieval *scientia experimentalis* has to take account of the fact that this covered a much wider range than the modern "experimental science." For example, Roger Bacon in his treatise *Scientia experimentalis*[18] uses in his claim for the rank and dignity of the subject the fact that theology is

---

[18] *Opus majus,* Part VI, *ed. cit.* II, and III (London, 1900); see M. Schramm, "Aristotelianism: Basis and Obstacle to Scientific Progress in the Middle Ages," in *History of Science,* ed. A. C. Crombie and M. A. Hoskin (Cambridge, 1963), Vol. II.

founded on the same basis. The distinguishing mark of *scientia experimentalis* seems to be that it is based on singular experiences, and these include the whole range of possible experiences from observations by means of the senses to mystical experiences and to the experience of reading particular statements in a book certified by its author's experiences or by divine revelation. In this range perhaps we have a reason for the intense medieval interest in this subject.

It is important to note also the natural scientific fields of inquiry in which the medieval conception of *scientia experimentalis* was developed. There were two main fields. One was medicine, including physiology and the investigation of the causes of diseases and of the properties of drugs. The other was "natural magic," which from the days of Roger to those of Francis Bacon included a definite set of subjects: optics, magnetism, machines for producing theatrically or practically astonishing effects by the harnessing of hidden sources of power, perpetual motion, alchemy, and astrology. This collection of subjects had accumulated since antiquity in Greek, Arabic, and Latin writings around the common idea of discovering the hidden powers of nature and harnessing them for a variety of theatrical or useful purposes. It was to convince the pope of the intellectual and practical usefulness of science that Roger Bacon sent him his *Opus majus* and other writings urging the need to promote better scientific education in the West. Bacon objected to the forcible conversion of conquered peoples such as he said was practiced by the knights of the Teutonic Order; science was part of the intellectual apostolate leading men to contemplate intelligently the work of the Creator known to Christians through revelation and, through this, leading unbelievers to the true Christian faith. It could also be put to immediate practical use by providing the rulers of Christendom with arms for protection against the forces of subversion within (directed by Antichrist, on whose agents he blamed the strange episode of the revolt of the *Pastoureaux* in France in 1251) and of Islam and the Tartars (under the successors of Genghis Khan) threatening from without. Bacon set great store by optics as a means of providing military intelligence and weapons. He said that Julius Caesar was said to have erected mirrors in Gaul with which he had observed what was happening in Britain; and he argued for the use of great burning mirrors to set enemy cities and camps on fire and of lenses to terrify those ignorant of their operation by making the sun and moon seem to fall down upon their heads —an early example of psychological warfare.

These associations of *scientia experimentalis* with "natural magic" explain why Roger Bacon should have found in his contemporary Pierre de Maricourt, the pioneer of the modern science of magnetism acknowledged by William Gilbert, his ideal of the "dominus experimentorum." It may help to explain also why experiment is so conspicuously absent from the normal methods of inquiry used in the academic natural sciences based on Aristotelian texts, notably from medieval dynamics and kinematics. Bacon described his conception of *scientia experimentalis* in the *Opus tertium* in 1267:

And this science certifies all natural and artificial things in the particular and in the proper discipline by perfect experience; not by argument, like the purely theoretical sciences, nor by weak and imperfect experiences like the practical sciences. And therefore this science is the master of all the preceding sciences, and the end of all theoretical argument. . . . One man I know, and only one, who can be praised for his achievements in this science. Of discourses and battles of words he takes no heed: he follows the works of wisdom, and in these finds rest. What others strive to see dimly and blindly, like bats in twilight, he gazes at in the full light of day, because he is a master of experiment. Through experiment he gains knowledge of natural things, medical, chemical, and indeed of everything in the heavens or earth. He is ashamed that things should be known to laymen, old women, soldiers, ploughmen, of which he is ignorant. Therefore he has looked closely into the doings of those who work in metals and minerals of all kinds. He knows everything relating to the art of war, the making of weapons, and the chase; he has looked closely into agriculture, mensuration, and farming work; he has even taken note of the remedies, lot-casting, and charms used by old women and by wizards and magicians, and of the deceptions and devices of conjurors, so that nothing which deserves inquiry should escape him, and that he may be able to expose the falsehoods of magicians. If philosophy is to be carried to its perfection and is to be handled with utility and certainty, his aid is indispensable. As for reward, he neither receives nor seeks it. If he frequented kings and princes, he would easily find those who would bestow on him honours and wealth. Or, if in Paris he would display the results of his researches, the whole world would follow him. But since either of these courses would hinder him from pursuing the great experiments in which he delights, he puts honour and wealth aside, knowing well that his wisdom would secure him wealth whenever he chose. For the past three years he has been working at the production of a mirror that shall produce combustion at a fixed distance; a problem which the Latins have neither solved nor attempted, though books have been written upon the subject.[19]

Within this scientific context, the complex of terms *experimentum, experientia, experimentalis* had a range of meanings extending from simple observation to deliberately contrived experiment. I shall give

[19] *Opus tertium*, cap. xiii, ed. J. S. Brewer (London, 1859), pp. 46–47; see A. C. Crombie, *Robert Grosseteste and the Origins of Experimental Science, 1100–1700* (Oxford, 1953), pp. 205–6.

some examples to illustrate the theory and practice of *scientia experi-mentalis* as a method of analytical inquiry.

In the essentially Aristotelian physical world that they accepted, the natural philosophers of the thirteenth and fourteenth centuries looked for explanations of phenomena in a particular way. They en-visaged the inquiry as a process of breaking down a complex observed phenomenon into the elements or principles involved in its production and then showing that these elements or principles provided the conditions necessary and sufficient to produce this phenomenon. This double process of argument had been known from its dual source in Greek mathematics and medicine as "analysis and synthesis" and was known from the time of Robert Grosseteste to that of Newton as "resolution and composition." In the thirteenth and fourteenth cen-turies the necessary and sufficient conditions were envisaged in terms of the four Aristotelian causes. To posit the four causes was to posit the caused phenomenon. Their commitment to the development of this approach logically and in experimental practice illustrates very clearly both the achievements and the limitations of the medieval natural philosophers.

There were two parts to the enterprise: first, to define what the phenomenon and its causal conditions were, and, second, to show how these causes brought the phenomenon about. For the first part, Grosseteste developed one characteristic type of argument, the *modus tollens* leading to a *reductio ad impossible* for choosing between pos-sible definitions and causes. The argument runs: "if p then q, but not q therefore not p." Grosseteste used it, in the short treatises he wrote on the nature of the stars, comets, the sun's heat, the rainbow, and other subjects, to eliminate certain explanations by showing that they led to consequences contradicted either by experience or by what he held to be established physical principles. For example, he rejected the explanation of the rainbow as a reflection of the sun's rays by a cloud acting as a large concave mirror because this would not produce either a bow or the reciprocal relation observed between the eleva-tions of bow and sun. Grosseteste used the *modus tollens* to choose between a limited set of possible explanations—a closed world of theoretical possibilities—mostly taken from earlier writers, and his invariable acceptance of the one remaining uneliminated explanation exposed him to the fallacy of affirming the consequent. It also con-siderably limited the use of experiment for the *exploration* of nature and exposed him to Newton's celebrated strictures on similar argu-ments used in the controversies over his new theory of color. This theory, Newton wrote, "was evinced by me, not by inferring ' 'tis thus because not otherwise,' that is, not by deducing it only from a

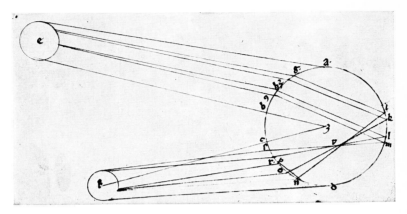

Fig. 1.—The paths of the rays inside a transparent sphere, from Theodoric of Freiberg's *De Iride*, II, cap. xviii–xx, Basel University Library MS F. IV. 30, fol. 21r (14th cent.). We may follow one "column" of light coming from the sun, *e*, and (incorrectly shown diverging) striking the sphere on the arc *qh*. On entering the sphere it is refracted to the opposite surface at *lm*, and thence is reflected internally. The reflected rays *lr* and *ms* intersect at *t*, and at *s* and *r*, respectively; the rays are refracted again on passing out into the air and so go (incorrectly shown converging) to the eye at *f*. In a raindrop the ray *hlr* is red and the ray *qms* is blue. (Figs. 1, 2, and 3 are reprinted from A. C. Crombie, *Robert Grosseteste*, with permission of the Clarendon Press.)

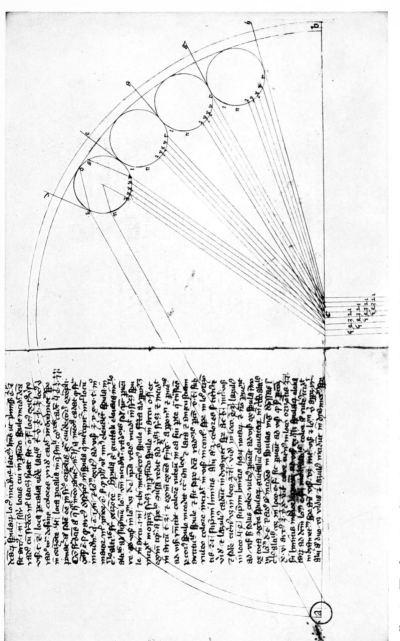

Fig. 2.—The formation of the primary (lower) rainbow, from Theodoric of Freiberg's *De Iride*, II, cap. xxxviii, fols. 33v–34r. The sun, *a*, and the four raindrops all lie on the "meteorological sphere" indicated by the large semicircle. The paths of the individual rays after entering each drop on the arc *ln* are not shown but would be as drawn in Figure 1, with the four colors emerging from the drop on the following small arcs: *tx* red (corresponding to *r* in Fig. 1), *xz* yellow, *xy* green, *yz* blue (corresponding to *s* in Fig. 1). Each of the four drops sends a different color to the eye at *c*, thus producing four bands of color one below the other: *de* red, *ef* yellow, *fg* green, *gh* blue. From the optical point of view this diagram contains several mistakes: if the incident rays going from the sun to all four drops were drawn, they would not all be parallel as they should be; the different colored rays emerging from each individual drop should be diverging instead of parallel; and all the rays of a given color emerging from the different drops should be parallel.

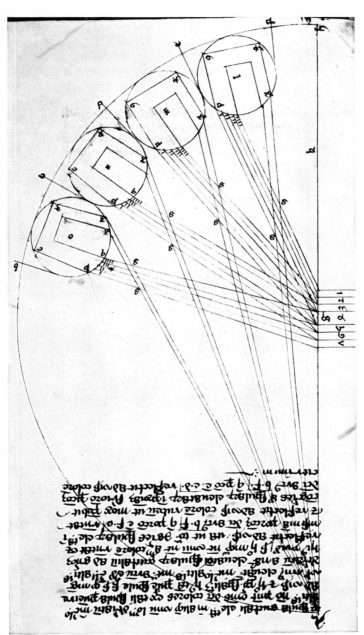

Fig. 3. — The formation of the secondary (upper) rainbow, from Theodoric of Freiberg's *De Iride*, III, cap. vi–vii, fol. 40r. The sun and four drops are shown on the "meteorological sphere" as in Figure 2. The incident sunlight *gg* enters each drop at *x* and is refracted; the colored rays (their individual paths not shown) are then reflected twice at *z* and at *c*, and refracted again on emerging into the air at *bd*. The four colors are marked: 1 red, 11 yellow, 111 green, 1111 blue. Each drop sends a different color to the eye at *g*, producing four bands of color in reverse order to those of the primary bow: *bc* blue, *cd* green, *de* yellow, *ef* red. The emerging colored rays are here correctly shown diverging, but the diagram contains the other two optical mistakes in Figure 1.

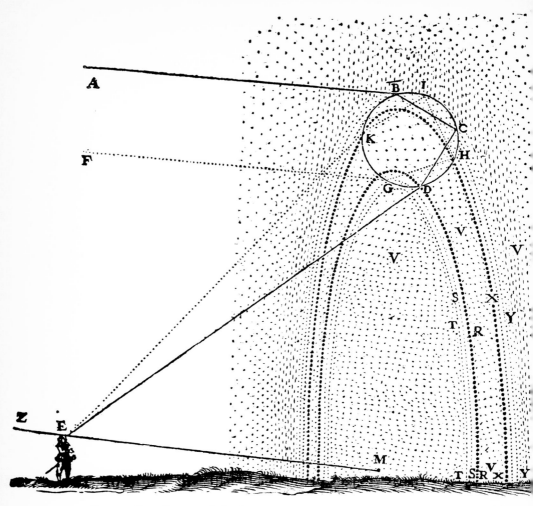

Fig. 4.—From Descartes's *Les Météores* (Leiden, 1637), Discours viii, showing the paths of the rays forming the primary (*A B C D E*) and secondary (*F G H I K E*) rainbows. The raindrop is enlarged. Note that here the sun's rays are correctly shown parallel.

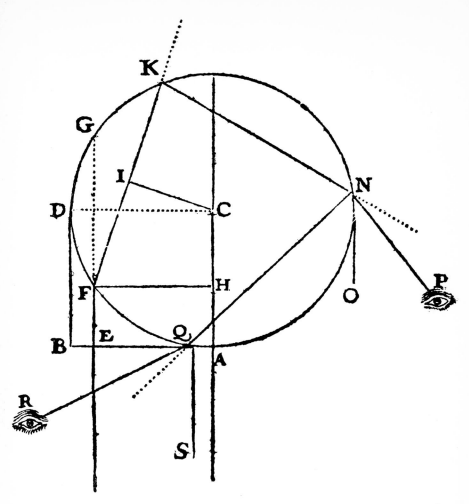

Fig. 5.—Descartes's diagram from *Les Météores*, Discours viii, used in calculating the paths of individual rays through a raindrop. A ray of sunlight incident at *F* passes through *F K N P* to form the primary bow and *F K N Q R* to form the secondary bow.

Fig. 6.—From J. Taisnier's *Opusculum perpetua memoria dignissimum, de natura magnetis et eius effectibus* (Cologne, 1562), showing his version of Pierre de Maricourt's automatic armillary operated by a lodestone.

E t a cesse sin que tu saches
Qil te fault faire z que tu saches
A toy ses vertus plus propices
P our mieulx paruenir aux premisses
D e vaillance cheualereuse
Et tout soit elle auentureuse
Encor te diray qui me maine
J ay vne mienne seur germaine

Fig. 7.—From Christine de Pisan, "Epistre d'Othea," Bodleian Library, Oxford, MS Laud. Misc. 570, fol. 28v (1450), showing Temperance adjusting the clock, indicating the place of moderation in human affairs. Below sit four virtues. This manuscript was executed for Sir John Fastolf in 1450.

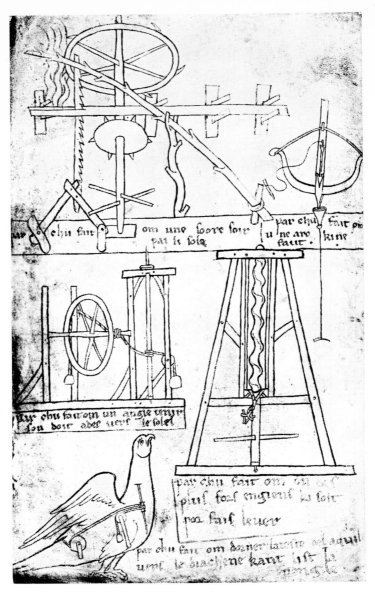

FIG. 8.—From the album of Villard de Honnecourt, Bibliothèque Nationale, Paris, MS français 19093 (13th cent.). *Top left*, a water-driven saw executing two movements, one to work the blade and the other to push along the plank being cut. *Center left*, is a device operated by weights for moving an angel set on the spike so that its finger follows the sun; this is the earliest known diagram of an escapement mechanism such as was used in mechanical clocks. *Bottom left*, a mechanical eagle. (Reprinted from A. C. Crombie, *Medieval and Early Modern Science*, Vol. I, with permission of Harvard University Press.)

confutation of contrary suppositions, but by deriving it from Experiments concluding positively and directly."[20]

But another type of argument was used in the thirteenth and fourteenth centuries for discovering causal connections by the exploration of nature. This was the "medical inductive argument" known through the writings of Galen and Avicenna and used by them to investigate the curative properties of drugs. Roger Bacon and others used it to define the rainbow as belonging to the species of phenomena including colors seen in dew and in sprays made by mill-wheels, squirting water from the mouth with the back to the sun, and other artificial means involving water drops, and to define the colors produced by a hexagonal crystal as a different species of the same genus (distinguished by not being circular) and the colors produced by iridescent feathers as belonging to a different genus. The rainbow, then, belonged to the species of colors produced by the refraction of sunlight through transparent drops or spheres. For a bow to be seen, a large number of discontinuous drops was required. "For," wrote the fourteenth-century French physicist Themo Judaei after experimenting with sprays, "where such drops are absent, there no rainbow or part of it appears, although all the other requisite conditions are sufficient."[21]

I may quote now the logical rules defined by William of Ockham for establishing causal conditions; they sum up the medieval achievement in this direction (in a way very suggestive of J. S. Mill) in a work that cries out for a modern edition, his *Super quattuor libros sententiarum*. He wrote:

Although I do not intend to say universally what an immediate cause is, nevertheless I say that this is sufficient for anything being an immediate cause, namely, that when this particular thing (*res absolutae*) is posited the effect is posited, and when it is not posited, all other conditions and dispositions being the same, the effect is not posited. Whence everything that has such a relation to something else is an immediate cause of it, although perhaps not vice versa. That this is sufficient for anything being an immediate cause of anything else is clear, because if not, then there is no way of knowing that something is an immediate cause of something else. For if from the proposition, that this being posited the effect follows and this not being posited the effect does not follow, it does not follow that this is the cause of this effect, then there is no way of knowing that fire is the immediate cause of heat in wood, because it would be possible

[20] *Philosophical Transactions*, July 8, 1672, p. 4004. Mersenne had said that some philosophers seemed to think that they had established an explanation as true because it had not been proved false, like a murderer whose claim to innocence has not been disproved (*L'optique et la catoptrique*, II, Prop. IV [Paris, 1651], 88–90).

[21] Crombie, *Robert Grosseteste*, p. 265.

to say that there is some other cause of this heat, which however does not act except in the presence of fire.

From this other consequences follow. One is that, when a universal cause is removed and the effect does not occur, this cause is an immediate cause just like a particular cause. Therefore, because in the absence of the sun generable and corruptible things are not produced, which however are produced by the mediation of particular causes, it follows that the sun is the immediate cause of them; unless perhaps you say that the sun is the cause of something else which is the immediate cause of them, but always that the sun is the immediate cause of something, namely either the effect or the cause of this effect, and this is enough for the proposition. Another consequence is that if, when either the universal or the particular cause is removed, the effect does not occur, then neither of them is the total cause, but rather each a partial cause, because neither of those things from which by itself alone the effect cannot be produced is the efficient cause, and consequently neither is the total cause. Another consequence is that every cause properly so-called is an immediate cause, because that cause which can be removed or posited without having any influence on the effect, and which when posited in other circumstances does not produce the effect, cannot be considered a cause; but this is how it is with every other cause except the immediate cause, as is clear inductively.[22]

Ockham restricted the immediate causes to the formal, material, and efficient, remarking that the "special characteristic of a final cause is that it is able to cause when it does not exist."[23]

To this "medical inductive argument" for establishing causal connections Roger Bacon had added a further important notion, that of prediction, taken from another element in this complex of fields in which medieval experimental science developed. This notion came from astrology.

One can examine history in past times and study the effects of the heavens from the beginning of the world, as in floods, earthquakes, pestilences, famines, comets, prodigies, and other things without number, which have occurred both in human affairs and in nature. After one has collected these facts, one should consult the tables and canons of astronomy, and one will find that there are appropriate constellations corresponding to each particular effect. One should then study with the help of tables similar constellations in the future, either near or remote as one wishes; and one will then be able to make predictions of effects, which will be similar to those in the past, since if a cause be posited, so is the effect.[24]

Bacon held that such predictions could not presume to certainty in particular instances and that men were not compelled to act against

---

[22] *Super quattuor libros sententiarum* (Lyons, 1495), Book I, distinction 45, q. 1, D.
[23] *Ibid.*, Book II, q. 3, G.
[24] *Opus Majus*, ed. Bridges, I, 389.

their will, but he said that astrology could throw light on the future by discovering general tendencies in the influence of the stars acting through the body on human dispositions as well as on nature at large.

Having discovered the formal definition of a phenomenon and of the conditions for its production, the second part of the inquiry aimed to discover the material and efficient mechanism by which it is produced. The best achievements of the medieval natural philosophers and the limitations imposed by their formulating of their problems in terms of the Aristotelian causes are exemplified by the remarkable treatise by Theodoric of Freiberg, *De iride et radialibus impressionibus*. A German Dominican who held high administrative office in the German Province, Theodoric tells us that he wrote this treatise at the request of the Master General, who spoke to him at the General Chapter held at Toulouse in 1304 and asked him to put the results of his researches into writing.[25] He seems to have died shortly after 1310, so its composition lies between these dates. Before *De iride*, Theodoric had written a treatise on physical optics entitled *De luce et eius origine*, which opens with the question put by God to Job: "By what way is light spread and heat divided upon the earth?" (Job 38). Theodoric said that the Lord had asked a difficult question if he was asking for the *causes* of the behavior of light, but that he would try to find them. He offered his explanation of the rainbow and other optical phenomena, as Descartes and Newton were to do, within the scheme of a general theory of light and color.

Theodoric began by citing Aristotle's *Posterior Analytics* to the effect that "it is the function of optics to determine what the rainbow is, because, in doing so, it shows the reason for it, insofar as there is added to the description of the rainbow the manner in which this sort of concentration [of rays] may be produced in the light going from any luminous heavenly body to a determined place in a cloud, and then by particular refractions and reflections of rays is directed from that determined place to the eye."[26] He recognized two main problems: first, how the colors were formed in each raindrop; and, second, how they were sent back to the observer in a definite number and order in an arc at a definite angle. Roger Bacon and Witelo (among others) had already tackled these problems and had given the angle of elevation of the radius of the bow as 42°, measured with an astrolabe. Witelo had also shown experimentally that, when sunlight was

[25] See William A. Wallace, *The Scientific Methodology of Theodoric of Freiberg* (Freibourg, Switzerland, 1959), p. 12; Crombie, *Robert Grosseteste*, pp. 242–43.

[26] *De iride*, I, cap. ii, in Crombie, *Robert Grosseteste*, p. 240; for the text of *De iride*, see J. Würschmidt's edition, *Beiträge zur Geschichte der Philosophie des Mittelalters* (Münster, 1914)), XII, 5–6.

passed through a hexagonal crystal or a spherical flask filled with water and the emerging colors thrown onto a screen, red was refracted least and blue most. In this way he explained the formation of colors, supposing that greater refraction progressively weakened the light so that it received progressive darkening from the medium. To explain the formation of the rainbow, he supposed that the colors emerging from one raindrop were reflected back to the observer by the convex external surfaces of the drops behind. The bow was an arc because the drops were spherical. The incident rays of sunlight were refracted and reflected through the same angle in each drop; Witelo had described a repetition of Ptolemy's experiments measuring the relation between the angles of incidence and refraction between air and water and other transparent media. The observer of the rainbow received rays of each of the colors from a set of drops standing in one of a set of concentric arcs one outside the other. If he moved his position, the observer would receive the colors from a wholly different set of drops.

Theodoric's mode of attack on the problem is notable, first, for his use of the *modus tollens* to reject Witelo's geometrical theory of the rainbow because this would not in fact yield the observations as claimed, and, second, for his systematic analysis of the formation of the colors and the paths of the rays in each drop by means of experiments with a hexagonal crystal and with a spherical glass flask of water and a crystal sphere used as "scale" models of a raindrop. These led him to a fundamental discovery: that the light was reflected back not from the convex external surfaces of the drops but from the concave internal surface of the same drop in which the colors were formed by refraction (see Fig. 1). He wrote:

Let the radiation enter the oft-mentioned transparent body and pass through it to the opposite surface and from that be reflected internally back to the first surface by which it originally entered, and then after passing out let it go to the eye; such radiation, I say, in as much as it is produced by a transparent spherical body, serves to explain the production of the rainbow. . . . Moreover, since, as was said above, any incident ray or radiation is not linear and indivisible but has depth and breadth like a column, therefore in any diagrams in the present work a light stream is represented by two lines bounding the light stream on either side.[27]

Using this discovery, Theodoric showed experimentally, by raising and lowering his model "raindrop" and covering now one and then another part of its surface, where the rays forming the primary and the secondary bows entered and emerged from the drop, and he

[27] *De iride*, II, cap. xviii; Crombie, *Robert Grosseteste*, p. 249.

worked out the geometrical paths of the colored rays inside. The order of the colors seen was the order of the drops sending them to the eye. He showed that the secondary bow was produced by two internal reflections and appeared about 11° above the primary (Figs. 2 and 3).

Theodoric's achievement was to discover the *mechanism* by which rainbows were produced. It was an achievement of the medieval method proceeding by a "resolution" of the complex phenomenon into the elements providing the formal, material, and efficient causes necessary and sufficient to bring it about. The limitations of this method of formulating and attacking a problem can be seen in Theodoric's failure to explain why the colors appeared only in narrow arcs of a definite size.[28] He fell back on saying that the position from which the rays returned to the eye was "in a place determined by nature."[29] He tried to account for the size in terms of the ratio between the distances from sun to raindrop and raindrop to eye, on the assumption that the sun and the drops forming the bow lay on a "meteorological sphere" centered at the observer's eye. For some reason, he used the value 22° instead of 42° for the angle of elevation of the radius of the primary bow. He also tried to connect this macroscopic ratio with the microscopic geometry of the raindrop through the size of the arc between the incident and emerging rays ($n\ z$ in Fig. 2) and by means of this to account for the formation of the different colors.

Exactly where Theodoric failed in dealing with this problem can be seen, as Carl B. Boyer has shown, by comparing his approach with that of Descartes. Ignoring the "meteorological sphere," Descartes saw that the key to the problem lay in the angle between the rays incident upon and emerging from the raindrops. The fundamental difference in approach is that Descartes then *calculated* the paths of rays falling at different angles on a raindrop and showed that in each case there is a clustering of rays emerging from the drop in almost the same direction, at about 41° for the primary bow and about 51° for the secondary (Figs. 4 and 5). Descartes used the law of refraction for his calculations, but Theodoric could in fact have made them using Ptolemy's figures relating angles of incidence and refraction, which Witelo had published. The fundamental difference between their approaches is that in defining the necessary and sufficient conditions for the occurrence of the phenomenon Theodoric concentrated

[28] See Carl B. Boyer, "The Theory of the Rainbow: Medieval Triumph and Failure," *Isis*, XLIX (1958), 378–90.

[29] *De iride*, II, cap. xxvi, xxx.

on the particular initial conditions whereas Descartes began with the general law.

The limitation on Theodoric's ability to deal with the problem of the rainbow was not technical but conceptual. The same limitation, imposed in different ways by Aristotelian natural philosophy on the best (as well as the worst) medieval science, can be seen in almost every field of inquiry. Two fundamental changes can be distinguished in methods of physical inquiry between Theodoric and Descartes. The first was a change in the concept of nature making the object of inquiry the discovery not simply of the causal conditions defining particular phenomena, but of universal quantitative "laws of nature." This meant a change from the logic of subject and predicate to that of relations expressed as algebraic functions. The second change was to make measurement essential to all physical research. These two changes seem to have had independent origins respectively in the theoretical quantification of academic science and in the practical quantification of technology.

(3) *Quantification in science and in technology*. Some hints that we have regarding the different intellectual needs and social pressures affecting quantification in science and in technology open a field of research bearing directly on the question of continuity and innovation in the origins of the modern scientific movement. I can only indicate some of them briefly.[30]

From the thirteenth century on, there are hints scattered widely through natural philosophical writings of the formation of a new concept of nature as a machine acting according to quantitative laws. For example, Grosseteste, Roger Bacon, Witelo, Theodoric of Freiberg, and other students of optics and related sciences made a distinction, amounting to that between primary and secondary qualities, between the physical activity by which such forms of efficient causality as light, heat, and sound are propagated and the sensations they produce when they act on the appropriate sense organs of a sentient being. This distinction came from the Greek atomists; but in the thirteenth century it marked a significant departure from Aristotle by conceiving the world of physical science as something removed from direct observation and something capable of mathematical characterization. Bacon made another move toward a new concept of nature by using the term *leges naturae* to refer to the "laws of reflection and refraction"[31] in a recognizably modern sense and by his development of the idea of a *natura universalis*, constituted by such laws, superimposed upon the system of particular natures making up the Aristo-

[30] See A. C. Crombie, "Quantification in Medieval Physics," *Isis*, LII (1961), 143–60.
[31] *Un fragment inédit de l'"Opus tertium,"* ed. P. Duhem (Quaracchi, 1909), p. 90.

telian universe. It was this "universal nature" that prevented the water from running out of the clepsydra, when the hole at the top was opened, by the "ordinatio corporum universi et mundi machinae congruentia."[32] Again, we find Pierre de Maricourt describing a perpetual motion machine made of a globular lodestone which, if mounted frictionlessly parallel to the celestial axis and inscribed with a map of the heavens, would by its daily rotation serve as a perfect clock (Fig. 6); and Pierre's contemporary Jean de St. Amand wrote: "Dico quod in adamante est vestigium orbis."[33] Later, after Buridan had ascribed the motion of the celestial spheres to the impetus originally given to them by God, which continued undiminished because there was no resistance, Oresme compared the celestial machine to a clock. Although he disagreed with Buridan and concluded that "it is not in the least like a man making a clock and letting it go and be moved by itself,"[34] this analogy was on the way to becoming as much part of the conception of the universe as the mechanical clock erected by Henri de Vick on the Palais Royal in 1370, seven years before Oresme wrote his *Livre du ciel*, was becoming part of the daily lives of Parisians (see Fig. 7).

By far the most systematic medieval attempt at the theoretical quantification of physics was that known as the "intension and remission of forms." Behind this lay the assumption that differences in all other categories could be reduced to differences in the category of quantity. The method then aimed to represent, for example, a change in the intensity of a quality such as heat in the same way as a change in a quantity such as length. The graphical and algebraic methods developed for representing amounts and rates of change, and the kinematical concepts and theorems developed by these methods, are among the most striking medieval contributions to physics. But even in this direction, medieval natural philosophers failed to break completely out of the Aristotelian concept of nature as expressed in the logic of subject and predicate, as distinct from that of functional relations, which they were beginning to develop. This whole development took place within a world of academic discussions that made stringent demands on logic, was mainly concerned with the method as such, and applied it to degrees of divine grace as well as of local motion; but it neither made a serious demand for measurement nor exposed any measurements that were made to more than a remote

[32] *Quaestiones supra libros quatuor physicorum Aristotelis*, ed. F. Delorme, in *Opera hactenus inedita Rogeri Baconi*, VIII (Oxford, 1928), 200–201; see Schramm, *op. cit.*

[33] L. Thorndike, "John of St. Amand on the Magnet," *Isis*, XXXVI (1946), 156.

[34] *Livre du ciel*, Book II, chap. ii.

chance of being checked by repetition. Moreover, at the root of this medieval quantification of natural philosophy lay two great inherited inconveniences: the use of the Greek pairs of opposite qualities (hot –cold, heavy–light, etc.) before the establishment of single linear scales, and the development of the mathematical methods in the Greek language of proportions.

The contrast between this academic world of theory and the demands made wherever a practical problem arose throws considerable light on the needs and pressures among which modern science grew up. In practical life it mattered if one was given short measure or the wrong product, was subjected to incompetent surgery, or arrived at an unintended destination. Measurement was essential to meeting the demand for accurate, repeatable results. So we find that measurement became a regular part of the procedure of an academic science like astronomy on which a practical demand was made for the calendar, for telling the time of day, and for navigation. The whole development of practical fields like navigation, surveying, cartography, gunnery, instrument making, commercial arithmetic and bookkeeping, architecture, painting by linear perspective, painting and sculpture from nature, assaying of ores and precious metals, prescribing of drugs of known properties, and diagnosis and control of disease depended on the growing technical ability to specify the conditions for producing the desired result; and these conditions became increasingly quantitative.

The discovery of the specific causal conditions that produced the effect was likewise the essential aim of the experimental science, just as the specification of the premises capable of yielding a given conclusion was that of logic and mathematics. In all these fields, the logic, mathematics, and natural and experimental science of the academic community and the technology of the skilled craftsmen, there was a growing sense of precision throughout the later Middle Ages. Medieval technical writings and the whole early history of instrumentation are still relatively unexplored, yet it is surely here that one must chiefly look for those habits essential to experimental science that were developed by the demand for quantitative accuracy made by the problems themselves. The existence not only of instruments but of medieval technical *writings*, the productions of literate men, is evidence of interested contacts between scholars and craftsmen from at least the early twelfth century. Two historical movements encouraged the further growth of contacts from that period: the rise in the social scale of such specialized craftsman as the *architectus*, and the enlargement of the scientific curricula of the universities. By the thirteenth century the result can be seen in such figures as Villard de Honnecourt (Fig. 8) and Pierre de Maricourt. Their successors were the "artist-engineers" of the Renaissance like Leo Battista Alberti and Leonardo da Vinci. I do not think that it was these men who created what was called in the seventeenth century the "new experimental-mathematical *philosophy*." This was the work of the successors of Robert Grosseteste and Nicole Oresme educated as natural philosophers and mathematicians in the universities. Their philosophical vision of an intellectual mastery through which nature could be subjected to human understanding and use descended from Roger Bacon's. But Roger Bacon's contemporaries could not solve many scientific problems, and they conspicuously lacked established standards of scientific cogency. The hints that we have suggest that the technical tradition of the late Middle Ages and the Renaissance played a decisive part in establishing the standards of modern experimental science. This is an open problem calling for historical investigation. Perhaps in these standards we have the real message of Western science to the world, for, in an intellectual tradition that has developed since Greek antiquity on the basis of the principle of noncontradiction, one distinction that has shone through all confusion is that between what one may want to believe and what is possible.[35]

I have given examples of the ideological (theological), logical, and technological preparation of the Western mind for its development of science and technology. If we are to include vision as well as problem-solving in the history of science, we really have no choice but to take seriously someone like Roger Bacon when he sets out as a "persuasion" (in the *Opus majus*) a program for acquiring intellectual and practical power over nature by mathematics and experiment. The later history of the origins of modern science is the history of the diversification of methods by which this program was deployed by Western Europeans in their aggressive attacks on nature and on the rest of mankind.

[35] See G. Beaujouan, *L'interdépendance entre la science scholastique et les techniques utilitaires (XIIe, XIIIe et XIV siècles)* (Les Conférences du Palais de la Découverte; Paris, 1957); A. C. Crombie, in *Critical Problems in the History of Science*, ed. Marshall Clagett (Madison, Wis., 1959), pp. 66–78; Lynn White, Jr., *Medieval Technology and Social Change* (Oxford, 1962).

GAINES POST

Law and Politics in the Middle Ages: The Medieval State as a Work of Art

To DISCUSS medieval law and politics on the occasion of the celebration of the founding of Rice University is not, after all, inappropriate. Our universities educate men for service in the legal profession and in the politics of government. So did schools and universities in the twelfth and thirteenth centuries. Indeed, Rice University belongs to the Middle Ages as well as to the twentieth century: it had its origin in a great medieval creation, the idea and institution of the university as a center of the highest learning of the age; and, as did the medieval university, it serves society and state.

From the twelfth century on, when the private law and rights of feudalism were still powerful, kings were engaged in the practical politics of trying to develop centralized governments. By 1300, particularly in England and France, such kings as Henry II and Edward I, Philip Augustus and Philip the Fair, were so successful that they had become the heads of sovereign, independent realms. Recognizing no superior, each king was emperor in his own realm.[1] The old ideal

GAINES POST is Professor of History at the University of Wisconsin. He holds advanced degrees from Harvard, and he attended the École des Chartes. He is a Fellow of the Mediaeval Academy of America and a Fellow of the American Academy of Arts and Sciences. He is the author of numerous articles on the legal history and political theory of the later Middle Ages and has been a Lecturer at the Riccobono Seminar and at the Medieval Institute of the University of Notre Dame.

This paper is based on a series of studies published during the past twenty years and on a study that will soon appear; these studies, slightly revised, will be published in 1964 by the Princeton University Press.

[1] For references and some aspects of the rise of elements of national sovereignty in this period, see my "Two Notes on Nationalism in the Middle Ages: I. *Pugna pro patria;* II. *Rex imperator,*" *Traditio,* IX (1953), 281–320; and " 'Blessed Lady Spain'—Vincentius Hispanus and Spanish National Imperialism in the Thirteenth Century," *Speculum,* XXIX (1954), 198–209. For other works on the subject and a good criticism of them, see Brian Tierney, "Some Recent Works on the Political Theories of Medieval Canonists," *Traditio,* X (1954), 612–25.

of the unity of Christendom in Empire and Church had failed. The principal theme of this paper is the role of legal ideas in the political action that created the early modern national state.

If able kings and political facts were important, no less important was the legal thought that originated in the law schools and universities and was transmitted by lawyers and jurists to royal governments. The theories of public law that these men found in the newly revived Roman law soon were penetrating royal councils and courts. Experts in the law became royal justices and they were influential as advisers of kings. They sometimes formulated the royal policy and the principles of political action. As a result, more and more frequently the legal terms from the public law of ancient Rome appeared in royal documents—for example, *utilitas publica* (public welfare), *status rei-publicae* (the state of the republic), and *status regni* (the state of the realm). (*Status* was the word also for public welfare; it usually meant in the context of public law the same thing as *utilitas publica*.) The new legal science, applied to the public law and the state, was effectively entering the realm of politics. It was furnishing the king with a legal justification for his public authority and for the use of his powers in the public interest—all at the expense of the old feudal order that had been state-less and even, in the public sense, law-less.[2]

Evidence will soon be presented. But, at the moment, given traditional ideas about medieval kingship, what I have said sounds like a gross exaggeration belonging to a desperate attempt to "modernize" the Middle Ages. Until recently the presumption has usually been that no state and no public law could have existed when people believed that all human life was subject to God and His moral commands and that, at least in spiritual matters, feudal monarchies were subordinate to the papal authority in the universal church. If some political awareness was practiced in the Machiavellian deeds of a few medieval kings, such as Philip Augustus and Philip the Fair of France and Emperor Frederick II, feudalism and private law prevailed.[3]

[2] See my paper, "The Theory of Public Law and the State in the Thirteenth Century," *Seminar* (Annual Extraordinary Number of *The Jurist*), VI (1948), 42–59; see also the studies that will be referred to in the following notes.

[3] This traditional interpretation prevails in Fritz Kern, *Kingship and Law in the Middle Ages*, trans. S. B. Chrimes (Oxford, 1939), esp. pp. 149–205. Nor does one find adequate emphasis on public law as such in R. W. and A. J. Carlyle, *History of Mediaeval Political Theory in the West* (6 vols.; Edinburgh and London, 1903–36); or in Otto Gierke, *Political Theories of the Middle Age*, trans. F. W. Maitland (Cambridge, 1922); or in C. H. McIlwain, *Growth of Political Thought in the West* (New York, 1932). Of course, one finds many sources quoted in these works that illustrate ideas of public law, but they are not used to show how the theory of public law and the state had developed as early as the twelfth century and the first half of the thirteenth. McIlwain, however, does call attention to what is really

Kings were no more than great feudal suzerains who had little knowledge of public law and were incapable of reasoned political action. Like other feudal lords, they were merely colorful children absorbed in "playing castle." Jacob Burckhardt long ago stated the traditional view: until the coming of the Italian Renaissance no prince had any concept of adapting means to the end. He meant, of course, that not until the fourteenth century, in Italy, did any political science related to the state and public law develop. Indeed, experts on the Italian Renaissance still assert that "reason of state" began in Florence in the fifteenth century. "The state as a work of art"—*Der Staat als Kunstwerk*—is a phenomenon of the Renaissance.[4]

And it is true that in the early Middle Ages no great appreciation of public law has been found—and on this I refer to two distinguished scholars at Rice University, Professors F. S. Lear and K. F. Drew, who have published careful studies of Germanic, Anglo-Saxon, Visigothic, Burgundian, and Lombard laws. As Professor Lear has said, treason was *infidelitas*, not *laesa majestas*.[5] If some revival of the Roman idea of public law and the state appears in documents of the Carolingian Age, the development of feudalism marked the triumph

public law in his *Constitutionalism Ancient and Modern* (rev. ed.; Ithaca, 1947)—with an excellent treatment of Bracton. Recently Walter Ullmann has done better with medieval ideas of public law, but he completely neglects my studies and even asserts that the idea of *utilitas publica* goes back to the Germanic king's duty to offer protection: "The principle of *publica utilitas* was . . . probably evolved from the *mundeburdium*, the supreme protection, inherent in the theocratic king" (*Principles of Government and Politics in the Middle Ages* [New York, 1961], p. 133). What he means by theocracy, which I cannot find in medieval ideas of kingship, I fail to understand. Anyhow, it is obvious that the concept of the public utility or welfare, which a government should achieve, is ageless; but in the Middle Ages it came chiefly from the Roman law—in the early period also from the tradition of the Roman Empire. As for those scholars who have been showing more specifically that ideas of public law and the state were important in the twelfth and thirteenth centuries, see below, n. 13.

[4] Burckhardt, *Civilization of the Renaissance in Italy*, trans. S. G. C. Middlemore (Harper Torchbooks ed.; New York, 1958), I, 26; also in *Gesamtausgabe*, ed. Werner Kaegi, V (1930), 4. See also references in my "*Ratio publicae utilitatis, ratio status, und Staatsräson*," *Die Welt als Geschichte*, XXI (1961), 10, n. 10; 98, n. 125. As for Burckhardt's *Der Staat als Kunstwerk*, it is the title of the first section of his classic on the Renaissance.

[5] Among Lear's studies the following are of special interest: "*Crimen laesae majestatis* in the *Lex Romana Wisigothorum*," *Speculum*, IV (1929), 73–87; "The Public Law of the Ripuarian, Alamannic, and Bavarian Codes," *Medievalia et Humanistica*, fasc. 2 (1944), 3–27; "Treason and Related Offenses in Anglo-Saxon Dooms," *Rice Institute Pamphlet*, XXXVII (1950), 1–20; "The Public Law and the Visigothic Code," *Speculum*, XXVI (1951), 1–23. Katherine Fischer Drew's studies are the following: trans., *The Burgundian Code* (London, 1949), and "I: Notes on Lombard Institutions; II: Lombard Laws and Anglo-Saxon Dooms," *Rice Institute Pamphlet*, XLIII (1956), v–ix, 1–125.

of private rights over the public interest of the state. But how long did this situation prevail? According to the traditional interpretation mentioned above, feudalism and private law remained predominant in England and France until the late thirteenth or early fourteenth centuries. Kingship, to repeat, was a private, proprietary right, not public; there was little public law, no practical concept of the public welfare, no state. As long as the king respected the rights of the great lords or magnates, his vassals, and the rights of the clergy and the Church, there was no need of political science, of statesmanship, of politics.

Yet feudalism itself, the feudal contract, had already opened the way to politics and to some awareness of the community of king and great lords. Any persistent royal violation of feudal rights could result in open resistance if not rebellion. So the magnates and prelates of England forced King John to sign the Great Charter and thus respect the feudal rights of the nobility. Another feudal source of politics was the principle, inherited from the Roman Empire and from early Germanic custom, that a king must, in all important and extraordinary affairs, obtain the counsel or advice of the great men of the realm. In theory, he enjoyed the right to make the final decision. In practice, if he accepted the advice of royal favorites and seemed to scorn that of the magnates who traditionally claimed the right to participate in counseling, a baronial party of opposition resulted. The principle involved was, in effect, the right to appeal from the king poorly informed (or advised) to the king better informed (or advised). The king should accept the counsel of those who claimed that they truly represented the welfare of the realm, which was allegedly being harmed by bad counselors. Politics thus become involved in the attempt of rival parties to control the king and his government. Such baronial opposition expressed itself in England in 1258–66 and again in 1311.[6]

The powers of the king in each case finally prevailed. The great men of the realm, however, were becoming increasingly aware of politics and of participating, not simply in a feudal society, but in a community of the realm, in the rising state and its problems.[7] The king and his government, on their side, in the very struggle to protect and strengthen the royal authority, were bound to make more frequent use of principles of public law, to appeal to the "public welfare" and "state" of the realm, and to understand the public nature of king-

[6] All this is so well known that references are not necessary.

[7] For an excellent and detailed appreciation of personalities and politics among the magnates in England, see Sir Maurice Powicke, *The Thirteenth Century* (Oxford, 1953).

ship in relation to the state as a whole. Feudal politics perhaps hastened the use, and the victory, of the concept of Roman public law, that the good state of the realm, the welfare of the state, was superior to all private rights, whether the rights of the king or the rights of his subjects. The public right of the king to rule for the public interest was no longer a private right of kingship.

This kind of politics, first based on feudal counsel and thereafter on new principles of public law, resulted in another important development: the rise of representation in what had been purely feudal assemblies. During most of the thirteenth century the magnates assumed that they were the effective membership of the corporate body or community of the realm of which the king was the head. Therefore, as provided by Magna Carta, if the king needed an extraordinary subsidy or tax for a war in defense of the realm, he must summon barons and prelates to his court, council, and assembly and obtain their counsel and consent. They represented all people beneath them and consented both for themselves and for the towns and knights of the shires, not to mention the peasantry. What they agreed to give the king had to be accepted by their inferiors.

By the end of the century, however, the right to be consulted, especially when taxation was the business, was extended to the knights of the shires and to towns. Why this happened is usually explained in four ways. First, the knights had become experienced in participating in shire courts and in "bearing the record" to the royal courts; and towns now enjoyed corporate rights connected with their greater wealth and prestige. Why should the king not make use of local administrative and political experience? Second, knights and leading townsmen were so important in their own right, and rights, that when the baronial and royal parties were at war in the 1260's, each party tried to get their support and began to summon their elected representatives to assemblies for debating what was proposed and consenting to it. Third, by summoning representatives of communities of shires and towns, the king could make his own propaganda for war and taxes more effective and obtain a more willing acceptance of extraordinary taxation than when the magnates alone were consulted and consented. Fourth, representation was a means of obtaining information about the taxable wealth of the realm.[8]

[8] In general, see M. V. Clarke, *Medieval Representation and Consent* (London, 1936), and George L. Haskins, *Growth of English Representative Government* (Philadelphia, 1948). For the element of propaganda, the best study is that by Joseph R. Strayer and Charles H. Taylor, *Studies in Early French Taxation* (Cambridge, Mass., 1939), pp. 21 ff. I have in the past been too critical of the emphasis on propaganda, but still I think that the legal concepts of procedural consent in *quod omnes tangit* were of more practical importance; see references to my studies in the following notes.

I am convinced that the addition of representatives to royal assemblies resulted also from the revival of the Roman law on corporations, agency, and consent. Communities of knights in the shires were treated as if they were corporations, and thus Roman corporate agency made true representation possible. If the business of the king affected their rights and they were summoned to Parliament, the knights of a shire could elect (usually) two of their colleagues as representatives and give them full powers (*plena potestas*) to defend their interests, in Parliament, before the king and his court and council.[9] But why, again, should the king summon communities to send fully empowered agents to a general assembly? The answer, I think, is that because of the increased recognition of the lawful rights of all free men, the magnates could no longer pretend that they furnished adequate representation and had the exclusive right to consent for others. This was because, in all probability, the Roman law had made king and people conscious of non-feudal principles of consent.

One Roman principle was this: when a case in court touched several parties in common, all must be properly summoned and thus be able to protect their rights.[10] In other words, the Roman law held that no court could decide a suit against any defendants who had not all been summoned and given the right to defend their interests. The principle was well known in England; for example, it was stressed by Bracton in his great work on the common law. Hence, if in Parliament the king was still the supreme judge and administrator of the realm, presumably he could not finally decide to levy an extraordinary tax without summoning all individuals whose rights were touched.[11] He had to summon, therefore, not only the great men but all lesser men whose rights were clearly recognized, and these could appear in Parliament only by sending representatives of their communities with full powers of attorney.

There was another principle of importance. It was stated in the maxim *Quod omnes similiter tangit, debet ab omnibus comprobari*—"What touches all alike, must be approved by all."[12] Edward I quoted

[9] This is treated in my "*Plena potestas* and the Consent of Representatives," *Traditio*, I (1943), 335–408.

[10] *D.* 42. 1. 47: "De unoquoque negotio praesentibus omnibus quos causa contingit, iudicari oportet. Aliter enim iudicatum tantum inter praesentes tenet." Cf. *D.* 42. 1. 63 and *C.* 7. 60.

[11] See my studies, "A Romano-canonical Maxim, *Quod omnes tangit*, in Bracton," *Traditio*, IV (1946), 197–251, and "The Two Laws and the Statute of York," *Speculum*, XXIX (1954), 417–32.

[12] *C.* 5. 59. 5: "ut quod omnes similiter tangit, ab omnibus comprobetur." In the *Glos. ord.* of Accursius, one finds *similiter* defined as *aequaliter*. See also my study, "A Romano-canonical Maxim," *Traditio*, IV, 200–209.

the maxim when he summoned representatives to Parliaments in 1294 and 1295. Now, in the Roman law *quod omnes tangit* expressed a form of voluntary consent. Did King Edward intend to say that the knights and other representatives had the full right to consent or to refuse consent to a new subsidy? Was democratic consent, limiting the sovereignty of the king, already at hand? Or was consent, even that voluntary consent expressed in the maxim, "What touches all must be approved by all," finally subordinate to the public authority of the king and to his decision of the business treated in Parliament?

My interpretation has in part been suggested already. Now let me explain it more fully. The king remained the supreme judge in his court and in Parliament. According to the Roman principles of procedural consent, when a "national" emergency or necessity was the *causa*, the king should summon all parties having rights touched by an extraordinary tax, for they all had the right to appear before the king and treat, discuss, and debate (*tractare*) why the king needed a subsidy and how much the king should reasonably get. Briefly, representatives of the communities of the realm, that is, the Commons, did have the right, along with the great nobles, to attend Parliament and participate in the business of king and realm. If they still usually accepted the leadership of the magnates, nonetheless they could organize their own body, the rising House of Commons, elect a Speaker, and present their views and complaints to the king. In enjoying the right to be heard, they were beginning to engage in politics and were becoming a political body. Soon they were able to secure "redress of grievances" in return for voting in favor of a subsidy. In a certain fashion, then, representatives—in England at least—were limiting the powers of the king.

Yet this limitation was not democratic; it did not reflect any theory or practice of popular sovereignty. Medieval representation was simply, in one sense, a means by which, on the one side, the king could directly extend justice and the protection of legal rights to all his subjects, to lesser as well as greater free men. In another sense, it was the means by which, on the other side, all communities of individuals could represent their rights in the king's High Court in Parliament. It did not as yet fundamentally change the constitutional fact that the king was the supreme judge, who was the interpreter of the law and whose final decision had to be accepted—if with much grumbling. Now let us see why this was so.

Traditional political theories had attributed to the king a prerogative that feudalism made ineffectual. But just when representative assemblies were arising, the revival of the public law of Rome enhanced the royal prerogative at the expense of feudal rights by relating the authority of the prince to the public order of the state. It gave to the monarchy a basis for political action against those who wanted to limit its powers. Despite all baronial resistance and efforts of representatives to control taxation, legal thought now stressed the ideas of the supreme public authority of the king. To be sure, private rights and privileges remained important; and the great lords of the realm were always to be reckoned with—as Richard II was to learn. Nonetheless, the public *status* of the king, his "estate royal," his "body politic" as opposed to his private body, and the rights of the crown, that is, the public powers of crown and "estate royal," remained indispensable to the "state of the realm" and superior to all private interests.

Of the many sources of theories of the "body politic" of the supreme royal authority, theories so well presented by Ernst Kantorowicz in his book *The King's Two Bodies*, the Roman law was as important as any.[13] For it was chiefly the Roman concepts of public law and the state that gave support to the political superiority of the kings of England and France—not to mention other feudal monarchies. The great Roman jurisconsult Ulpian stated the theme for the jurists and royal councilors of the twelfth and thirteenth centuries. "The public law," he said, "is that law which deals with the state of the Roman Republic"; it dealt also, he continued, with religion, the priesthood, and the magistracy.[14] Professors of law at Bologna were quick to teach that this meant that the public law was the "constitutional" law of the state, providing both for the maintenance of the public welfare (the *status*) of the republic and for the government that was necessary to this end. Without magistrates, they declared, there could be no law and justice, no public welfare, no state. It was the public right and duty of the prince and his magistracy "to preserve the state of the Republic lest it perish"—so said Hugolinus, Azo, and Accursius, famous legists of the late twelfth and early thirteenth centuries.[15]

13 Princeton, 1957. My debt to Professor Kantorowicz and his studies is great indeed. Valuable also, for their appreciation of ideas on the public law, are studies by Sir Maurice Powicke and Joseph R. Strayer, referred to in my "*Ratio publicae utilitatis,*" *Welt als Gesch.*, Vol. XXI, pp. 11 f., nn. 13, 15; also Strayer, "Defense of the Realm and Royal Power in France," in *Studi in onore di Gino Luzzato* (Milan, 1950), I, 289–96. And now, H. G. Richardson and G. O. Sayles, *The Governance of Medieval England from the Conquest to Magna Carta* (Edinburgh, 1963), is valuable for the emphasis on the public authority of the King and on the influence of learned men in the government.

14 "Publicum ius est, quod ad statum rei Romanae spectat. . . . Publicum ius in sacris, in sacerdotibus, in magistratibus consistit" (*D.* 1. 1. 1. 2).

15 See the *Glos. ord.* of Accursius to *D.* 1. 1. 1. 2; I have quoted Hugolinus and Azo from unpublished glosses to the same passage in the Paris, BN, MSS lat. 4461 and 4451.

If the theory of government for the public welfare included the traditional ideal of ruling according to law and justice, for the common welfare of the subjects of the prince, it now included also the idea that the powers of the king were a supreme necessity, else the state itself could not flourish or even survive. Is it strange, then, to discover that as early as 1200 the lawyers were saying that, in one sense, the magistracy was itself the public *status*, the essence of the state? The *status* of the Republic, said one legist, was the *potentia*, the public power; *status, id est, magistratus,* said others. Within a century, in fact, it was not uncommon to hold that the "state" of the realm was the king, and the "state" of the church was the pope.[16] No king, of course, said that he was the "state" of the realm or that he was the state. But the king enjoyed a public *status*, the "estate royal," precisely because he must have the power that was necessary for the maintenance of that other public *status*, the public welfare and safety of the realm. The "estate royal" was the supreme authority of the king, and it was also those rights of the crown of which Bracton spoke, rights that pertained to doing justice and maintaining peace in the realm.[17]

Frequently, however, constitutional historians of England have argued that the estate of the king, *status regis*, was his revenue, or the private aspect of kingship. Yet the definition of *status* as the public authority or powers of the king occurs in English sources as well as in the Roman lawyers. In 1177 Richard Fitzneale, in the famous *Dialogue of the Exchequer*, defined the *status regis* or "estate royal" as the royal *potestas*. Several documents of the thirteenth century give the same meaning.[18] I feel certain, therefore, that the statement in the Statute of York, 1322, that a business pertaining to the *estat* of the king and *estat* of the realm and the people must be treated and established in Parliament, refers to the public authority and powers of the king in conjunction with the public welfare of people and kingdom.[19] This meant that no political party of barons had the right to change the constitutional powers of the king. What was done in Parliament was done with the king's authority after consultation with the magnates and representatives constituting the community of the realm of which the king was the head.

Now, if the estate royal was, in terms of public law, indispensable

---

[16] Details in my forthcoming study, *"Status, id est, magistratus* and *Status regis,"* soon to appear in *Studies in Medieval and Renaissance History,* I (1964).

[17] Stubbs, *Select Charters* (9th ed., Oxford, 1913), p. 413; on Bracton, see *inter aliis* Kantorowicz, *King's Two Bodies,* pp. 143–92.

[18] *S. C.,* p. 200.

[19] Besides my "Two Laws and the Statute of York," *Speculum,* XXIX (1954), 417–32, the study referred to above, n. 16, gives details.

for the preservation of the "state" of the realm, the power of the king was public, was exercised for the public interest, and was potentially far stronger than in feudal law. It was not merely the monarch's duty, it was his right, to do what was necessary to maintain the public welfare or "state." Evidently the "public welfare" clause from the Roman law was rapidly becoming a principle that was more on the side of the royal authority than on the side of the king's subjects and their private rights. Indeed, a well-known Roman maxim was that private rights must yield to the public law and the public welfare.[20] Consequently, whenever the "state" of the realm was in danger, whenever a dire emergency arose (for example, an aggressive attack on the kingdom), the king could lawfully wage a just war of defense and demand sacrifices of all his subjects in order to meet the danger.

This public right of the king to decide on actions for the defense of the state meant that he should use "right reason," that is, the "reason" of the public welfare, not the "reason" of his own private rights or selfish aggrandizement. "Reason of state," in fact, was becoming a principle of public law.[21] What was "reason of state" in the Middle Ages, and how did it hasten the development of the political authority of the royal government?

As early as the middle of the twelfth century, Hugo of St. Victor, theologian and mystic, said that when *reason* and *necessity* concurred, the royal authority had the right to tax the clergy. John of Salisbury, that great classical humanist of the twelfth century, included public *ratio* in his general theory that the state is a "work of art." His premise is that God, by means of nature and the natural law, approves human society. Organized society, however, the state and its government, is the product of human reason and skill. Because God and nature endowed men with the faculty of reason, above all it is the duty of the king as head of the corporate body of the realm to imitate nature by using reason in all public or political business. By steadily practicing the art or skill of governing with the aid of reason, the king is engaged in making the state a work of art.[22] How, then, should the prince use reason and skill in the science of politics? John, good Christian that he was, believed that the king should use his reason above all in obeying the command of God to be just and rule according to the highest

[20] "Ius publicum privatorum pactis mutari non potest" (*D.* 2. 14. 38); the legists in the *Glos. ord.* of Accursius frequently assert, as a maxim, that the *utilitas publica* (or *communis*) must be preferred whenever it is in conflict with private utility.

[21] What follows on "reason of state" is based on my study, "*Ratio publicae utilitatis,*" *Welt als Gesch.,* XXI (1961), 8–28, 71–99.

[22] On nature, society, and the state, and on the "state as a work of art," see John's *Metalogicon,* ed. Webb, I, i, viii, xi; II, Prooem; IV, xv; and *Policraticus,* ed. Webb, V, ii, ix; VI, xxi–xxv.

principles of justice and equity. He should therefore protect all lawful rights of people and churches and maintain the law in his courts. In other words, John says, the prince should take care of the welfare of the republic and always submit his will to reason and the common good. Indeed, John says literally, the "reason of the common welfare" is itself a principle of law and equity; and it demands that the king should possess no more horses, servants, and baggage than the "reason of necessity or utility" requires for the "reason" of the good of the people. (How much "baggage," I wonder, should our president and his government possess for reasons of the public welfare of the United States?) In brief, according to John, "reason of state" is the right reasoning in the public interest of the realm and of the people. God commands it—and the state itself becomes a positive good rather than a necessary evil.

Essentially the same principle, if more down to earth, was a commonplace in the ideas of the lawyers trained in the new legal science. They held that the just war of defense was a supreme reason and necessity for extraordinary taxation. At least two decretists as early as 1200 spoke of the "reason" of the defense of the fatherland. The legists agreed, and Accursius even said that if a son unavoidably, in battle, killed his father among enemies who were attacking the fatherland, he was not guilty of patricide. "Fight for the fatherland!"—"*Pugna pro patria!*" Such was the frequently stated imperative. To die for the fatherland, it follows, was to win eternal glory. (Let me remind you that the independent realm of France or England was already, in the thought of some lawyers, the "common fatherland," that is to say, a fatherland that superseded all local loyalties, just as the common fatherland of the United States sometimes takes precedence even over devotion to Texas.)

The "reason" of defense, moreover, justified deceit against the enemy and made *dolus bonus*, "good deceit" (the "Holy Pretence" of a later age), a lawful principle of government.[23] The moral law of God was always fundamental. But *casualiter*, in cases of necessity, of dire emergency, or of the "just cause," when either the *status regni* or the *status Ecclesiae* was in danger, a compromise (the choice of a lesser evil or a lesser good for the sake of the greater good) was lawful. Indeed, according to the canonists as well as St. Bernard of Clairvaux, the necessity of preserving the "state of the Church" gave the pope supreme authority over the Church and the clergy. A famous secular theologian, Gérard d'Abbeville (about 1260), went so far as to assert

---

[23] See George L. Mosse, *The Holy Pretence* (Oxford, 1957); for the medieval canonists, see my references in "*Ratio publicae utilitatis,*" *Welt als Gesch.*, XXI (1961), 96, n. 123.

that if the emperor were a Saracen who threatened the faith, the pope could grant dispensation to a nun from the vow of chastity and from the "religious habit" in order that she might marry and convert the infidel and thereby prevent the destruction of the Church and the faithful. This the pope could do *ratione utilitatis communis*, by reason of the common utility.[24]

No doubt Gérard's lesson in "reason of the Church" was purely academic, a classroom exercise, so to speak. But even a purely hypothetical *casus*—this was true casuistry—shows how important the reason of necessity and utility was for the authority of any prince. The magistracy, in fact, said the glossators, was a supreme necessity in itself, else the state and law and justice could not exist. Is it surprising, then, that well before 1200 we encounter the words *ratio status regis?* And first, literally, as far as I know, in England, when the great Henry II was consolidating the central government. Richard Fitzneale, in the *Dialogue of the Exchequer*, exalted the *ratio status regis* as the "reason of the public powers" of the king.[25] By reason of this "state of the king" all subjects should serve him with their wealth. At the same time, in Italy, a glossator, Johannes Bassianus, was saying that the *ratio honoris publici* (reason of public office) existed for the *ratio publicae utilitatis*.[26] Consequently, by reason of his public estate, the "estate royal," the prince was above the law with respect to his duty and right to preserve the state of the realm, *ratione publicae utilitatis*. As early as the twelfth century, then, the double reason of *status regis* and *status regni* was a general reason of state—the *raison d'être* of the public authority of a king was governing with reason in the public interest.

Not only did the reason of the public welfare in cases of necessity give the ruler the right to ask for subsidies and wage a just war. According to the Bolognese jurist Azo,[27] the king of France, Philip Augustus, could allege the "reason of the public utility" of making peace as a justification for sacrificing the private, feudal rights of Arthur of Britanny to King John. Whether Philip actually did so is not certain. But kings were learning from the public law how to make feudalism bow to the interest of the state—of course, they still had a long way to go!

A part of the process of defeating feudalism was the use of the

[24] From a *Quodlibet* in the Paris, BN, MS lat. 16405, fols. 51 f., *De voti sollempnis dispensatione;* details in my "*Ratio publicae utilitatis,*" *Welt als Gesch.,* XXI (1961), 26 f.

[25] Stubbs, *S. C.,* p. 200.

[26] Quoted in my "*Ratio publicae utilitatis,*" *Welt als Gesch.,* XXI (1961), 72.

[27] See the *Quaestio* discussed by Azo in *Die Quaestiones des Azo,* ed. E. Landsberg (Freiburg i. Br., 1888), pp. 86 f.

Roman legal theory that special privilege or franchise, accompanied by jurisdiction, was not an immunity, in the old feudal sense, but a delegation of powers that remained subordinate to the royal authority. Such franchises, like the County Palatine of Chester or the French *apanage*, were granted not for the private utility of the great lord but for the "reason of the public welfare" of the whole realm. A distinguished scholar, Helen M. Cam, has, in fact, shown how the royal prerogative in England remained superior in jurisdiction and in policies related to the safety of the community of the realm.[28] All lawful privileges, so canonists and legists were saying, were a recognition of the special merits of those who had served and would continue to serve the state. Privileges were lawful only if granted *ratione publicae utilitatis*.[29] A noble doctrine if not carried too far!—as it was in the later Middle Ages and on into the eighteenth century, with bad results for the state even under the so-called absolute monarchs of the seventeenth and eighteenth centuries.

By 1250, it is now evident, the medieval doctrine of reason of state was well formulated. (It even made the public law protect the private rights of women in dowries: dowries and marriage interested the state as well as God; the procreation of children in lawful matrimony was manifestly for "reason of the public welfare"; and it certainly was for the public welfare, as one jurist said, to have a child who might become pope.)[30] At the end of the thirteenth century, it is almost needless to say, the principle was repeated over and over when powerful, national monarchs were challenging the universalism of the church under Pope Boniface VIII. If "necessity" was the more frequent word, the publicists and legists sometimes said *"ratio"* too. So Pierre Dubois repeated the old theme that the "reason of necessity" permitted the king to tax the clergy in order to finance the proposed great Crusade. Pierre de Belleperche, an able French legist who became one of Philip the Fair's advisers, specified a demonstrably lawful *ratio* and *causa* for the confiscation of property in order to feed a hungry royal army. The French monarch skilfully employed the principle against Pope Boniface VIII, who obviously was threatening the "state" of the whole corporate body of France—so said the king in his propaganda. And everyone knows how Edward I spoke of the dire emergency that, in Philip the Fair's alleged threat of aggression against England, touched the *status regni* and all the people, clergy and laity, in common; and how, at the same time, Philip was arousing the French with emotion-

28 "The Evolution of the Mediaeval English Franchise," *Speculum*, XXXII (1957), 427–42; also my *"Ratio publicae utilitatis,"* *Welt als Gesch.*, XXI (1961), 78, n. 73.

29 In my *"Ratio publicae utilitatis,"* *Welt als Gesch.*, XXI (1961), 78.

30 See *ibid.*, p. 80.

stirring accusations against the English. What could poor Boniface VIII do but tacitly admit that both kings were fighting a just war of defense against each other and that in such a dire and immediate emergency and necessity they could go ahead and tax the "national" clergy without waiting for his approval? Even the champion of the papacy, Giles of Rome, like Hugo of St. Victor, agreed to this. In the early thirteenth century, a canonist had said: "But nowadays all wars are unjust!"[31] By 1300, the triumph of "reason of the necessity" of the safety of the state had forced the pope to admit that all wars between national states were just. In other words, the new national states, under the leadership of kings and jurists who skilfully used "reason of state" as a political weapon, were beginning to disrupt the ideal of Christian unity within the Church.

So far, except for calling attention to Gérard d'Abbeville and his theory of the pope's authority in terms of the "reason of the common utility" of the Church and the faithful, I have emphasized the legists and canonists. Now let us turn again to scholastic philosophers and theologians. No doubt they seldom personally advised kings and assisted in formulating royal policy. But the two whom I have in mind (there were others, of course), namely, Thomas Aquinas and Henry of Ghent, reveal that "reason of state" was accepted in the philosophy and theology of the later thirteenth century.[32]

To put it briefly, Thomas Aquinas says that the prince should use "right reason," under the control of prudence and justice, to the end of the common good of all citizens and of the safety of the state. He recommends no cynical, non-moral appeal to necessity. He assumes that "reason of state," if properly understood, should result in no violation of the moral commands of God. If in one instance he observes how the safety of the city may demand the violation of the statutes of the city itself, he fails to think of the possibility that it may demand the sacrifice of the life of a few for the sake of the many. The case is this: a statute forbids the opening of the city gates when the enemy is approaching; nevertheless, a gate can be opened to citizens fleeing the enemy and seeking refuge behind the walls. What Thomas fails to debate is whether, if the enemy is in such close pursuit that it will endanger the city to open the gate, it is morally lawful to shut out the citizens seeking refuge and cause their death. The legists, I think, would have said that of course the gate should remain closed: the necessity of the safety of the city knows no law, not even the divine

[31] For references in this paragraph, see my *"Ratio publicae utilitatis," Welt als Gesch.,* XXI (1961), 80–85.

[32] *Ibid.,* pp. 85–92, for details from the theories of Thomas Aquinas and Henry of Ghent.

command "Thou shalt not kill." (We have already seen that in legal thought—and it was in the Christian tradition too—it was not a sin or crime, during a just war of defense, to kill the enemy. *Pugna pro patria!* And it was glorious to die for the fatherland.)

Henry of Ghent is possibly more interesting than Thomas Aquinas because he is relatively more practical in his theory. If the state is a natural end in itself, he held, and its common good is more divine than the good of any individual, it is also the *patria* that men should fight and die for. Naturally, a prince or king, as the head and representative of the body of the community, is necessary for the achievement of the end of the public welfare in law and order and in the safety and existence of the state.

This general theory of Henry is well known; however, his arguments for the power of the king need elaboration, for he associates the royal legislative authority literally with *ratio status*. He debates this question: Are the subjects of a king bound to obey a statute that is allegedly made for the common utility, when the common utility is not evident? (This refers to Ulpian's statement [*D.* 1. 4. 2], well known to all the legists, that the emperor cannot make a new law that changes an older law unless it is for the "evident utility.") In general, he answers, subjects are not bound to obey their prince in those things that do not meet their own wishes unless those things are necessary for safety. A statute that is not for "evident utility" or necessity is not, therefore, binding.

If, however, a statute or law that is not "evidently useful" orders subjects to pay a tenth of their goods as a tax, must they obey? No, Henry says, for a tax levied when there is no evident utility or necessity (for the defense of the community) is an arbitrary confiscation of property. But if the king levies a tax for just cause, that is, the public welfare and safety of the state, his subjects must pay. For the very office of the prince exists for the safety and peace of the republic, which are also the interests of all citizens as parts of the state. All citizens are born for the republic, and it is glorious to die for it; so all, king and subjects alike, are bound to work for the state as their end on earth. Everyone, therefore, is bound to obey the laws and to pay taxes that are necessary for the safety of the state. Indeed, subjects must obey even when it is not *evidens* that a tax law is necessary. Why? Because the prince should be deemed so superior in all virtues that in a certain manner the good of the whole community is in him, and his good is the good of each and every person in the state. (He was the state!) His subjects, then, should obey his statutes even when they are not sure that they are "evidently" for the common utility. They should believe that the statutes were made for the public utility because they should have confidence in the wisdom and goodness of the prince and his counselors.

In fact, Henry continues, it must be presumed that the king is prudent and industrious in legislating for the public welfare; it must be presumed that he is mentally superior, for the people gave their consent to him and his acts when he started his reign. Above all, this presumption of the king's wisdom and his ruling for the public welfare is *ratione status!* Literally, for "reason of state," then, it is presumed that the monarch is always acting for the public welfare. What does Henry of Ghent's *ratio status* mean? Our reason of state? Almost, but not quite. In one sense, given the context of his argument, it is the *ratio publicae utilitatis* or the *ratio status regni.* More strictly, like the *ratio status* in the *Dialogue of the Exchequer,* it is probably the reason of the public office of the king. Whatever the meaning, if it is necessary for the safety of the realm, Henry concludes, the prince can compel his subjects to pay a tenth of their goods—and not only a tenth, nay a half, even the whole, even themselves! The ruler should be certain, however, that the exaction is really for the public utility. His statutes must be so "reasonable" that they proceed not from the *potentia* of fact, but from the *potentia* of law. The king's power is not absolute, for it is regulated by the deliberation or weight of that reason which does not err! Reason that does not err is obviously the right reason of the public welfare and security and peace of the state, reason rightly interpreted by the supreme authority by reason of his public *status.* Again, essentially, the *ratio status reipublicae* and the *ratio status magistratus* are in harmony as two aspects of one "reason of state."

It is now clear, I think, that in Henry of Ghent and in the general legal thought of the thirteenth century, "reason of state" was already modern even though its use was subordinated to God and His moral commands. A principle of public law, it demanded that the government reason rightly by acting wisely and speedily in order to preserve the state. In times of great danger, the end of the safety of the state justified the means adopted by the king on the basis of "right reason." The necessity of state knew no law—*salus populi suprema lex!*

The state was itself becoming a moral end, for it was approved by God and the law of nature. It will amuse you to hear how a philosopher of the late thirteenth century indirectly confirms this statement. Is adultery, he asks, ever lawful? No, never! But suppose (a *casus*, hence, casuistry) a tyrant is threatening to destroy the city. If a good citizen is suspicious but can learn about the plot only by sleeping with the tyrant's wife, is adultery then lawful or good? Again, no! But it is a lesser evil. The end, the safety of the state, justifies the means.[33] (I am

---

[33] *Ibid.,* p. 96, n. 122.

happy to say that Machiavelli's Prince did not have to resort to adultery in order to maintain his *stato!*)

In sum, "reason of state" in the twelfth and thirteenth centuries was a principle of medieval "constitutionalism." On the one side, it was related to the steady business of good government according to law and justice; on the other, to the special case of reason and necessity when the state was in danger. Altogether, it represented the constant belief in the use of reason about problems of government and the state. "Reason of the public welfare" or "reason of the state of the realm" is, therefore, one of the keys to understanding how medieval kings combined the public law with politics and created the early modern state. Royal "reasoning" in terms of the public welfare explains how the prerogative remained with the king. The king and the law were sovereign, not the people. (If in our democratic constitution sovereignty lies chiefly in the people, in the hands of our presidents and other magistrates, "reason of state" and the "public welfare clause," in times of national emergency and in the building of superhighways, are still principles of public law enhancing the powers of government rather than the rights of the people. How can it be otherwise? The safety of the state and the reason of progress and the public welfare know no law. Even in a democracy the "public welfare clause" can be tyrannical.)

One more observation about medieval kingship. When Philip the Fair and his counselors were discussing policies with regard to the quarrel with Pope Boniface VIII, they issued no reports on what was said in council meetings about the actual use of "reason of state" in declaring a national emergency.[34] There is no way of knowing whether any of Philip's advisers, or indeed Philip himself, argued cynically that the public and the world should be deceived by appeals to reason and necessity or whether, in sincerity, God was called upon to approve any action that would preserve the state of the realm. And we cannot know what debates took place in the royal council when the decision was made to use every kind of Machiavellian means necessary for accusing the Knights of the Temple and destroying their Order. Alas! no scribbled notes and minutes from council meetings have been found in royal wastebaskets in the Archives Nationales. (Let me remind you that debates in our presidential cabinet meetings can hardly be studied by the historian. Who can write the history of the cabinet on the basis of statements made by a columnist for the newspapers?

[34] Joseph R. Strayer, in "Philip the Fair—a 'Constitutional King,'" *American Historical Review*, LXII (1956), 18–32, has convinced me that Philip IV was no figurehead but a leader in his government, that he understood what his counselors advised and assumed responsibility for all decisions. Yet Strayer himself has revealed no details of the discussions in the royal council.

What, for example, was said about Cuba? And, to recall "ancient" history, what did Mr. Eisenhower and the members of his cabinet say about the U-2 flights over Russia? Did they argue in favor of *dolus bonus*, useful or good deceit, and in favor of appealing to the necessity of the defense of the nation?)

The history, then, of meetings of royal councils in the Middle Ages cannot be written. Yet the terminology of necessity, emergency, public utility, and "state of the realm" appeared in the royal documents that were issued as a result of plans agreed on by the king and his counselors. Beyond doubt, therefore, in the twelfth and thirteenth centuries, kings and their legally trained advisers fully understood essential principles of public law and consciously practiced "reason of state." The modern state was at hand; it was the "work of art" of medieval lawyers and the "estate royal"; it was the result of political action rationalized by the new political science of public law.

What "reason of state" is today, in the minds of presidents of the United States, I do not know. It is the principle, I dare say, of the constant use of reason for the public welfare and safety of the people and the common fatherland of all fifty local fatherlands; it is the reason of secrecy and "good deceit" (*dolus bonus*) in politics and government; it is the reason of defending the state in times of danger or necessity. Who can doubt that God protects America and approves its *Status, ne pereat!* Perhaps medieval Roman law and politics did contribute something to American constitutionalism—*Magna Carta* does not explain how the President and Congress enjoy a great political advantage over the sovereign people when, in cases of national emergency, "Necessity knows no law." At any rate, our universities train those who go to Washington in order to counsel presidents on how to practice the art of statesmanship. Substantially created in the Middle ages, university and state remain closely associated in the realm of public law.

E. DWIGHT SALMON

Medieval Foundations of Modern History

It is a truism long recognized in the historical profession that every age rewrites its own history, that is, its own version of the past and its own interpretations of the past. In celebrating its semicentennial of distinguished contribution to American education, it is especially appropriate that Rice University should sponsor a series of lectures on medieval studies. These past fifty years have seen a significant rewriting of the history of the Middle Ages, one that has produced new scholarly approaches and revised earlier judgments. Because this fruitful historical scholarship has contributed to a better understanding of the modern period, some of the relationships between these two great historical epochs deserve consideration.

In a sense, historians today are facing a crisis of courage, the courage to employ older techniques of the historian's craft, to search for evidence by rigorous research (one of the contributions of medievalist to modernist), to interpret and synthesize that evidence and those facts in strictly historical terms. The medievalists have resisted the temptation to replace the older standards of the craft by relying on new terminology to give a meretricious appearance of profundity. For today it needs to be stated that novelty and a pseudoscientific vocabulary do not guarantee deeper and clearer insights.

There is a Spanish proverb, says E. K. Rand, citing George Santa-

E. DWIGHT SALMON is Winkley Professor of History at Amherst College. He is a graduate of the University of Rochester and of Harvard. His research is in the area of early modern history with special emphasis on the Spanish Empire of the sixteenth and seventeenth centuries. During World War II he was attached to the Historical Section of the United States Army and was Chief Historian of the North African and Mediterranean Theater of Operations and aided in placing the Army Historical Program on a permanent basis. In 1946 he served as academic adviser to the National War College, where he lectured on Spain, and from 1946 to 1955 he was a member of the Secretary of the Army's Advisory Committee on the History of the Army. He has received the Legion of Merit award, Officer of the Order of the British Empire, and the Medaille de la Reconnaissance Française. He is author of *Imperial Spain*.

yana as his authority, that every good house contains a wine cellar and every good sermon a quotation from Augustine. Similarly it may be said that every historian who talks about his craft begins by discussing theories of history. From the Greeks through the Church Fathers, notably Augustine and Orosius, down to the present, there have been many attempts to define our field of knowledge and its utility. "Es ist alles so unendlich compliziert," said one of the German professors, and Voltaire, Napoleon, and Henry Ford added their contributions to this difficult problem. Lynn White has wittily reversed Voltaire in his statement, "History is a bag of tricks the dead have played on Historians." In his Trevelyan Lectures at the University of Cambridge in 1961, Edward Hallett Carr chose as his title *What Is History?* and answered that "it is a continuous process of interaction between the historian and his facts, an unending dialogue between the present and the past."[1] Another distinguished British historian, Alan Bullock, has said: "No man can sit down to write about the history of his own times—or perhaps of any time—without bringing to the task the preconceptions which spring out of his own character and experience. This is the inescapable condition of the historian's work."[2]

The truth of this is manifested in two ways: first, in the historian's selection of material (Carr says "facts") and his interpretative emphases for a given period, both of which reflect his conscious or unconscious reaction to the prevailing interests of his own time; and, second, in the process of historical revision of values and judgments.

Examples of the first are numerous. Between my entering college in 1913 and the postwar period of the twenties came the rise of economic history in widespread popularity, partly as a consequence of a greater realization of the role of economic factors in the supply, financing, and conduct of World War I and the problems of recovery in a war-torn world. That is not to say that economics had had no place in history, but certainly the spread of industrialization had widened the awareness of the peculiar importance of that factor in all societies. From J. R. Seeley's dictum, "History is past Politics, and Politics present History," to the detailed study of institutions, of legal and constitutional history, and of political theory, we can see a shift in interest from the mid-nineteenth century. In this development a historiographical contribution of the medievalists is evident, for it was their exact scholarship and textual mastery that led naturally to the work of the legal historians. The great work of the political theorists in tracing the ideas underlying authority and rights from the Greeks through the Middle Ages had pertinence and raised searching ques-

[1] E. H. Carr, *What Is History?* (London, 1961), p. 24.
[2] Alan Bullock, *Hitler: A Study in Tyranny* (New York, 1952), p. 9.

tions relevant to the study of institutions today. C. H. McIlwain in his study of the origins and *raison d'être* of authority and liberty took as his text Rousseau's "Man is born free and everywhere he is in chains. . . . What can make it legitimate?" His work and that of his students, one of whom, the authority on *majestas* and *potestas*, is a member of the Rice University faculty, have shown another example of the continuous stream from antiquity through the Middle Ages to present political realities.

The 1920's also saw the emphasis on social history, with its analogies in the study of manorial relationships and urban classes in the medieval towns. Despite the uneven records of the situation of the peasant on the manor, barely mentioned in legal documents or contemptuously treated in the bourgeois *fabliaux*, the agricultural worker did receive attention, and his transition or escape to the status of free town-dweller became the focus of fruitful studies. The turbulent life of the town and the drive of the bourgeoisie to economic and political power mark the central and later Middle Ages, and as they became the objects of historical consideration the way was pointed to similar treatment of the social aspects of the modern period. Medieval urban development also has furnished essential background for economic historians of the Commercial Revolution and the growth of early modern industry and banking. Conspicuous too is the contribution of the Middle Ages to one of the most recent special interests in historiography: intellectual history, or the history of ideas.

The second factor, the process of historical revision, interestingly and very pointedly for the Middle Ages, illustrates the live and flexible character of historiography. In a recent lecture, Sidney Packard pointed to the last forty years of medieval scholarship as a striking example of historical revision.[3] He cites the changed views of feudalism, of the manor, of the twelfth-century monarchy, and of the weakening of the Roman Empire, and he cites also the spectacular work in the history of technology occasioned by the revisionary discovery of the influences on the medieval West of the Chinese, Indian, and Moslem worlds. It is revealing to note that George Burton Adams said in 1906 that there were no more problems to be solved for the period of the fifth to ninth centuries and that Dorothy Whitelock said in her inaugural lecture as Elrington and Bosworth Professor of Anglo-Saxon at Cambridge in 1958 that as a graduate student thirty years before she had been afraid that there was nothing more to be learned about Anglo-Saxon history. The reversal of the older view of Anglo-

[3] Sidney R. Packard, *The Process of Historical Revision: New Viewpoints in Medieval European History*, Katherine Asher Engel Lecture, Smith College (Northampton, Mass., 1962).

Saxon influence on Europe and of Saxon survivals after the Norman Conquest has taken place in the intervening years.

A similar example from the historiography of the modern field lies in the impulse that started Frederick Jackson Turner on the study of the American West and the frontier. He related that at the conclusion of his first year in Herbert Baxter Adams' seminar at Johns Hopkins, Adams said that the seminar had now exhausted every possible topic in American history and would turn to Europe the following year. Turner, raised in Wisconsin, suddenly realized that the West had been ignored, and thus he began that lifetime study of such great importance to the history of our own country.

There was a time when it would have seemed absurd to suggest that Gibbon's verdict on Rome's fall would be revised, save in minor details. But in spite of the revisions of the nineteenth-century historians in the direction of constitutionalism and the later concern with such economic and social explanations as the drain of specie, Oriental influences, and depopulation caused by the spread of marshlands, mosquitoes, and malaria, the monumental image of a Decline and Fall stated in Gibbon's orotund Roman periods remained a historical constant. Yet revision of judgments on the causes of Rome's fall continues to produce a series of vital historical studies. One may mention the nationalistic reappraisal and rescue of the early Germans by Dopsch and his school and the stimulating effects of the Pirenne thesis. The great Belgian medievalist, by the writings of his critics no less than by his own revolutionary theory that Rome "fell" in the seventh century rather than in the fifth, made a fundamental revision of the dating and circumstances of the empire's demise. From Pirenne's emphasis on the urban situation in the Roman lands and the effects of the Moslem inroads into the Mediterranean there developed a new view of the history of the early Middle Ages. In this connection, Robert Latouche's recent work on the economics of the Dark Ages places Pirenne's *Mohammed and Charlemagne* high among the great historical achievements as an original interpretation, creating controversy and expanding knowledge.

William Carroll Bark, in examining the "Problem of Medieval Beginnings," maintains that the socioeconomic historians like Bloch, Dopsch, and Pirenne have been primarily destructive and, while attacking the Gibbonian "causes," have not produced a new consensus to replace the old. He offers another revisionary thesis: a new civilization was emerging in the West as the political machinery of the later Roman Empire was weakening, so that the early Middle Ages saw a pioneer society taking shape, living on its own physical and intellectual resources, which were reduced qualitatively in some ways but which were Christian, creative, and very much alive. There are many other instances of new interpretations of the origins of the Middle Ages.

Thus we see that historical study of the medieval period is far from static; it is constantly receiving new scholarly impetus. A long-standing, rather envious, and plaintive reproach directed to the medievalists by the historians of the modern period is that they have the great advantage of working with sources that are closed and limited. New material may come from the spade, but not from the archives, the *Monumenta*, and the Cartularies or Pipe Rolls. Unlike the modernist, the medievalist does not have to cope with the printing press and with ever proliferating documentary sources. Therefore it is instructive to note that the revisions of medieval scholarship carry over and furnish another type of foundation for the history of the sixteenth to twentieth centuries. Moreover the canon is not unchangeably fixed: John La Monte advocated centering attention on the Byzantine and Levantine East instead of the Latin West in the history of the Middle Ages; others suggest the Slavic and Moslem East, the technological keys to development, and so on.

While we are considering these aspects of the historian's craft, it is interesting to note that in his lectures on the study of medieval and modern history, Bishop Stubbs divided modern history at the French Revolution into a first period of "a history of powers, forces and dynasties" and a second period in which "ideas take the place of both rights and forms." This notion that "ideas" characterize the history of the nineteenth and twentieth centuries has a modern, even current, ring and is consonant with the tenets of the intellectual historian. But as far as the material of history is concerned, it ignores completely the inescapable—in truth the essential—role of ideas in the history of the Middle Ages. One has only to think of the patristic writers, of the Scholastics, or of Dante to realize that the history of ideas is not a peculiarly modern phenomenon.

But in the large, the role of medieval history as a substructure for modern history requires a consideration of a host of influences on later times that the time span of the Middle Ages and the historian's interpretation of that span have bequeathed to man's knowledge of his past. Leaving aside the vexed question of the precise dating of that series of centuries between classical antiquity and the conventional definition of modern times, we have for a long period accepted a rough limit of a thousand years, give or take some at either end, which scholars have studied as a bloc. At the chronological end nearest to us, we can detect a world recognizably like our own in some aspects of man's activity, changing imperceptibly, rapidly, or even not at all for years to come. These influences may be examined as study of the Western world, starting with the sixteenth century and moving onward, reveals continuity in human development from the earlier time span and throws light upon fructifying earlier elements in radically changed patterns of the later era, which we conventionally call "modern." In the whole range of culture, in political relationships and institutions, in economic and social structures, in technology and invention, and in geographical knowledge expanding as the result of European discoveries by sea and land, with their concomitant effect of new types of empire-building, and in contacts with non-European peoples and civilizations—in all these the historian of the modern period owes many debts to the medievalist. These legacies of the Middle Ages have been listed by Friedrich Heer of the University of Vienna as follows:

A few great medieval institutions are still with us: constitutional monarchy, parliaments, trial by jury, the Roman Catholic Church, and universities. The university, and the intellectualism it nurtured, is a specifically European phenomenon. In the universities were laid the foundations of the scientific culture of our modern world, in them grew up the habit of disciplined thinking, followed by systematic investigation, which made possible the rise of the natural sciences and of the technical civilization necessary to large industrial societies. . . . Although it was much else besides, the intellectual life developed in medieval Europe was a positive response to the broad stream of classical, Arab, Islamic, and Jewish influences to which it was exposed.[4]

To these he might have added the Greek or Orthodox Church which is still with us, changed rather less from its early form in doctrine and liturgy than its Western rival.

To attempt to deal with all the legacies from the Middle Ages to the later world would manifestly be beyond the scope of this paper. I shall therefore consider only a few of the aspects of the modern historical inheritance from the medieval past—and those largely in the early modern period. As Edward P. Cheyney pointed out in his inaugural as president of the American Historical Association, the unity and continuity of European history across the ages is a leading characteristic, although the process of change is also at work, as it is in all human activity. Without trying to obscure the differences between the two conventional periods, it is interesting to note that their histories flow in a generally continuous line.

As we know only too well, history, no less than Scripture, has often

---

[4] Friedrich Heer, *Mittelalter*, trans. Janet Sondheimer as *The Medieval World, Europe, 1100–1350* (Cleveland, Ohio, 1962), p. 190.

been quoted by the Devil to his purpose. The Middle Ages, with their popular labels of darkness, ignorance, savagery, and bigotry, have been sufferers at the hands of the vulgar. "Medieval" is a handy epithet of derogation in everyday journalese. But at the upper levels of statecraft, we have a sinister example in Hitler's Reich. The Führer's tame philosopher, the crackpot Balt, Alfred Rosenberg, turned to the German Middle Ages to justify Hitler's *Drang nach Osten* as the resumption of the mission of the Teutonic Knights to conquer and replace the inferior, non-Nordic Slavs. Rosenberg also glorified the Teuton by asserting that the great figures of medieval Italy were Nordics who had crossed the Alps, and he added, "It is today certain that Dante was of Germanic ancestry [because his name came from] Durante Aldiger, a pure Germanic name."[5]

From a consideration of some facets of the historiography of the Middle Ages, it will be profitable to look at the transition from those centuries to the modern era. First, of course, is the fact that the very name *medii aevi* is the invention of the Italian humanists of the transition period of the Renaissance. Therefore, our central topic demands an examination of the relationship of the earlier period to the time of transition. The contempt that those self-confident classicists of the fifteenth century felt for their predecessors long irritated medieval scholars; Henry Osborn Taylor wrote his two-volume *Thought and Expression in the Sixteenth Century* without once using the word "Renaissance." To use that term would be to admit that there was a revival of the classics or indeed a need for revival.

Although the Italian humanists are responsible for the term that has survived and although in their sense of rediscovery of the "pure" form of the classical languages they saw a distinction between their own age and the preceding ages, they are not responsible for the periodization of later historiography. The men of the Renaissance were vividly conscious that they were living in a new age and in a changing culture. They thought that the centuries intervening between their own and antiquity were dark and sterile intellectually, stultified by the deadening hand of the church. But they could not be expected to see their period as a whole, living in the midst of it, and their interests were limited to classical learning and the fine arts. The idea of rebirth, of a glorious dawn after a long night of darkness, appears in the writings of the humanists in Italy and north of the Alps. Wallace K. Ferguson has pointed this out and has warned us that we must not read into Renaissance cultural metaphors "a too clear conception of the distinctive character of the new age as a whole

---

[5] Alfred Rosenberg, *Mythus des 20 Jahrhunderts* (Munich, 1938), p. 70 n.

and of its historical relation to the past."[6] It was to be the later historians who took over the humanistic argument and regularized the periodic divisions of the history of the West that we have inherited.

In historical writing, the Renaissance burgeoned, as might be expected from the humanists' awareness of the historians of Greece and Rome. Like their prototypes, the humanists wrote formal histories with polish and with critical acumen, but with their attention directed solely to wars and politics. In other connections, they dealt with art and literature, but they ignored economic and social topics or the life of contemporary people. Although the chronicle form died out slowly, the Renaissance treatment resembles Comines more than Ordericus Vitalis or Matthew Paris. Like all historians, the humanists reflected their own day, and the contrasts with medieval historians are notable. Individuals and parties became important. Instead of seeing all history as the unfolding of God's plan, with the Fall and Redemption giving meaning to all the past, with the Four Kingdoms and their fate as historical evidence of the plan and hence the representation of history in universal guise, Renaissance historiography became nationalistic and concerned with national states. The *Weltanschauung* of St. Augustine gave way to that of Machiavelli and Guicciardini, of Comines, Alonso de Santa Cruz, and Polydore Vergil.

Another characteristic marks the break with the Middle Ages: the new history is secular and ceases to be a handmaid to theology, portraying the Christian epic. But here again the break is not sharp; Otto of Freising had seen the decline of the empire, and while that decline was consistent with the notion of a sinful world approaching its final judgment, it was a political decline. Similarly, Dante's theory in the *De Monarchia* fits the framework of universal Christendom in good medieval fashion, but its aspiration and its hope are for a political solution. The national emphasis rather than the universal and the secular rather than the religious mark the chief differences between the two periods' views of history. The humanist historians, however, as they wrote history, gave the lie to the role they assigned to the Middle Ages. For example, Flavio Biondo wrote a history of the decline of the Roman Empire from 412 to 1412 in which he deplored the weakening of Rome and the breakup of the Empire but rejoiced in the revival of Italy through the growth of the communes. There is no idea here of a Renaissance, nor is there in Machiavelli's *Florentine History*, "from the decline of the Roman Empire" to the rise of the

---

[6] Wallace K. Ferguson, *The Renaissance in Historical Thought: Five Centuries of Interpretation* (Boston, 1948), p. 2. This book treats in masterful fashion the problems of the period of medieval-modern transition.

Medici in 1434; the Middle Ages as a period are not damned, and it is contemporary Italy that is dark and forbidding.

Because in conventional chronology the Renaissance is the historical phenomenon next to the Middle Ages and because its humanists suggested the term, cultural features and contrasts are germane to our general topic. A striking contrast is the intellectual break of the Renaissance with the medieval university, a break that involved the decline in influence of the "Queen of the Sciences," theology, and was pointed by the scorn of the humanists for logic and the scholastics. Although the humanists' influence upon learning was profound, it did not extend to scientific knowledge, whose advance in the early modern period was outside the activities of that group.

What is true in general of the Italian Renaissance holds for the Renaissance in the northern lands. Here the nationalism emerging in the later Middle Ages is more strongly ingrained than in Italy and colors both humanism and historiography. Moreover, northern humanism, as exemplified by Erasmus and some of the Germans, turned in the direction of religious reform. The tie of the Renaissance with Protestantism carries us further from medieval religion and the universal church. Generalizations in this area are peculiarly dangerous. Humanism is different in France, in Germany and the Low Countries, in England, and in Castile. Rabelais and Bodin are humanists no less than Erasmus. In general culture and in national historiography, there is more of a break from and less continuity with the medieval past.

After dwelling on the immediate postmedieval period in its cultural phase, largely because if there had been no historical Middle Ages, there could have been no concept of a Renaissance, it is instructive to turn to the counteroffensive of the medievalists. This came about as a result of extensive research, during the last forty years or so, into the intellectual and cultural history of the Middle Ages. Another example of historical revisionism, this study of an area that for years had produced sound scholarship on political institutions opened a virtually new field. The work of a great scholar and great teacher, Charles Homer Haskins, had much to do with the increase of medieval studies in the United States. In 1927 his *Renaissance of the Twelfth Century* revised the opinion held since the publication of Jacob Burckhardt's *Civilization of the Renaissance in Italy* in 1860 that medieval learning was arid, that it produced no good Latin literature, no classical appreciation, and no secular study. In this book and in his scholarly *Studies in Medieval Culture* (1929), Haskins demonstrated the rich cultural attainments of the High Middle Ages, not only in Latin literature and contemporary writing, but in the university, in the translations from Greek and Arabic, so essential to the advance of science and philosophy, in the revivals of those two fields of learning, and in the revival of jurisprudence centering at Bologna and utilizing the *Digest* of Justinian's *Corpus juris civilis.* Haskins did not deny the accomplishments of the Italian Renaissance, but he did maintain that that movement was "not so unique or so decisive as has been supposed." German scholars had treated earlier bursts of intellectual activity such as the Carolingian Renaissance and the Ottonian Renaissance, but as isolated phenomena in the midst of general darkness, rays of light that flared and then flickered out. What Haskins did (and the host of scholars who have followed him) was to show an essential continuity between the cultures of the Middle Ages and those of the modern era.

There is not time to trace the extensions of this revision into all the related medieval fields that have received new scrutiny by students of medieval humanism, by romantic worshippers of a purple-hued Middle Ages, or by neo-Thomists and other religiously-oriented scholars. But among historians of science there have been interesting revisions of judgment. Starting in 1913 with Pierre Duhem's work on classical and medieval cosmology came an appreciation of the scholastics' concern with the world of nature. The authoritative studies of medieval science have been among the most impressive of the specialized fields of medieval investigation. It is interesting to note that such scholars as George Sarton and Lynn Thorndike hold that the Renaissance writers marked a decline from the Middle Ages and that science did not regain the medieval level until the later sixteenth and the seventeenth centuries. Sarton said that the Renaissance from the scientific point of view was "less a genuine revival than a halfway rest between two revivals."

On the other hand, James Conant in his lectures *On Understanding Science* argues that it was the Renaissance humanists who by turning back to Greece carried forward the "dispassionate search for truth" that prefigures the modern scientific attitude. His contention is that though the use of critical reason "was kept alive more by those who wrote about human problems than about natural phenomena," the process was useful for later inquiry. He holds that it was the men of the Renaissance who turned to nature and gave us the great scientific revolution that began about 1540 and lasted until 1700. Myron Gilmore's discussion of the critical scholarship of the humanists (in *The World of Humanism*) stresses their provision of the texts of Greek science and philosophy in Latin versions with commentaries and indicates the influence of Pythagorean and Platonic thought on Copernicus, who studied at Bologna under Domenico Maria de Novara, a member of the Neo-Platonic group in Florence. These differences, lying somewhere between a scientific spirit of inquiry and a knowledge of specific fields, show how difficult it is to fix an exact line of descent from medieval to modern times and to award praise or blame for continuity or rupture of influence between the Middle Ages and the Renaissance.

Time and space do not permit consideration of such other sides of the Renaissance as the development of the fine arts, vernacular literature, political structure, economics, or the religious revolution of the Protestant Reformation. In some of these activities, the dividing line of 1500 is meaningless, for there is an evolutionary tie with the Middle Ages rather than a sharp break in continuity.

Land warfare is one example of continuity; for it became recognizably modern in the sixteenth century although it had its roots in an earlier period. The tactical and organizational innovations of the "Gran Capitan," Gonsalvo de Córdoba, which produced the Spanish infantry, had their origins as far back as the early fourteenth century at least. Also antecedents for the increasingly decisive use of fire power or missile power can be found in the Byzantine employment of Greek fire and in the mounted archers of the Mongols with their short bows of laminated horn, in the Norman archers of William the Conqueror, and in the English bowmen of the Hundred Years' War. Now the arquebus had replaced the bow and the mingling of pikemen with arquebusiers or musketeers had given the foot soldier tactical advantage over the mounted warrior. Confidence had returned to the infantry as in the days of the phalanx, the legion, and the *Heer* of the early Germans, as the bazooka was to give the GI confidence in holding his own against the modern tank during World War II. The final relegation of the cavalry to a subsidiary role in battle and to a position as a merely aristocratic symbol had started in the medieval period even when the knight (thanks to the introduction of the stirrup, as Lynn White has pointed out) still dominated Europe.

Another, similar example can be found in naval warfare, notably in the long conflict of the Christian galley navies of Charles V and Philip II against the Moslem galleys of Suleiman the Magnificent and his North African corsair vassals. Although the development of the caravel from the clumsy medieval round-ship had by 1500 produced an efficient sailing ship with adequate sea-endurance for long voyages, a ship that brought a distinctively different warfare to the great oceans, still, in the Mediterranean, the galley was king through the sixteenth century. That virtually tideless sea permitted the rowed long-ship to dominate the water in war and in commerce just as the same type of ship had dominated the Mediterranean from antiquity through the Middle Ages. This period, however, saw the rowed ship improve until the great war galleys of Spain, Venice, and the other Italian maritime states, the Papal navy, and the Turk reached a size of 120 oars to a side, with as many as seven rowers to a sweep. The introduction of guns did not change galley tactics, because the normal system was to place two guns on fixed mounts at the bow, a system necessitating a turn of the entire ship to traverse. Naval tactics had depended on the same maneuvers for centuries: to ram an opponent, to sideswipe him and break his oar blades, and to board him for close combat by the large complement of infantry that each galley carried. In these particulars, the continuity from the Middle Ages and antiquity is marked.

It is in the area of naval strategy and its interaction both with politics, dynastic and international, and with religious conflict that the century departs from its medieval predecessors. Control of the sea now became a necessity of statecraft. Unlike the medieval ruler whose naval requirements were sporadic, Charles V and Philip II could never ignore the Mediterranean in their planning. Because they had to maintain a two-ocean navy, with a sailing fleet in the Atlantic also, and because ship-building has never been cheap, the financial difficulties of the Spanish crown are easy to understand. Moreover, the control of the great sea took on a modern rather than a medieval cast. In a modified version of Mahan's doctrine, state power demanded control of the water. The conditions of galley operations created a special strategic situation because in spite of Ranke's contention that the Turkish victory of Prevesa over the combined fleets of the Emperor in 1538 gave the Moslems "control" of the Mediterranean until the Christian victory of Lepanto in 1571, the truth is that in the intervening period ability to use the sea freely and to deny its use to the enemy depended on which side concentrated a galley fleet in any particular cruising season. Bear in mind that galleys had low sea-endurance and could not keep to the sea for long periods as could the ocean-going galleon or "great ship." For the sake of economy or because other commitments prevented, there were years when either Spain or the Ottoman did not concentrate, and the ships of the adversary moved freely about the Mediterranean. To this extent, sixteenth-century conditions modified the full force of Mahan's definition of sea power. Likewise this factor partook more of medieval maritime power than of modern, but on the whole Mediterranean strategy departs from the Middle Ages now and parallels that of the sailing ship and of the open ocean.

Usually treated as a part of the Renaissance because of the vast expansion, literally and figuratively, of European horizons, the Era of Discovery shows the debt of the modern period to the Middle Ages. The work of the Portuguese prince, called by nineteenth-century historians "Henry the Navigator"—a grandson of John of Gaunt through his mother Philippa of Lancaster—was pivotal. The great advancement of navigational sciences and cartography resulted from his establishment of a library and observatory at Sagres in 1418 and his gathering scientists from many lands there. In the nearby port of Lagos, Henry's shipwrights perfected the caravel, improving earlier Italian designs and producing the seaworthy sailing ship without which long voyages on the stormy oceans would have been impracticable. The driving force was Henry's, and when the captains he sent out passed Cape Bojador on the Atlantic coast of Morocco and returned to report the waters to the southward sweet and pleasant, there vanished the psychological barrier that had kept Christian sailors from venturing beyond that cape toward the equator. Those waters had been feared to be so hot that ships would take fire, filled with pressure ridges that would swamp a ship, and so near the equator that the ship's company would be turned black by the sun. By Henry's death in 1460, his expeditions had explored and charted the coast of West Africa to 2° south latitude and had occupied the Atlantic islands of the Azores, Madeiras, and the Cape Verdes. From these beginnings were to come in succession the Portuguese circumnavigation of Africa, landfall on Brazil, establishment of posts on the Malabar coast of India, Ceylon, the Malacca Straits, the Spice Islands and others of the East Indies, in Japan and on the Chinese coast, and of course Columbus' great voyages across the Atlantic and Magellan's circumnavigation of the globe.

This broadening of the European world, with all its fateful consequences down to the year of grace 1963, must not blind us to the medieval substructure of the discoveries. Prince Henry himself was a curious blend of the modern and the medieval and therefore a genuinely transitional figure. An experimenter and innovator, skeptical of many older traditions about geography, he was at the same time an extreme ascetic who had vowed perpetual chastity, the Master of the Portuguese monastic order of Jesus Christ (a crusading order from the Reconquest), and a champion of a revived crusade. Part of his motivation for exploring the African coast was to find the mouth of the rumored western branch of the Nile with the intention of sending a crusading expedition up that river to unite with Prester John (the central figure of another persistent medieval legend of a Christian potentate ruling on the other side of the Moslem lands) and to attack Islam from the rear. His captains followed Henry's instructions by venturing up the mouths of the Senegal and Niger rivers to test the western Nile theory. The acquisition of the African coast with its riches of gold dust, ivory, and slaves, previously exploited by Arab seamen who named the region Bilad Ghana (whence the European name of "Guinea"), would serve to finance Henry's crusade as well as to enrich Portugal and extend geographical knowledge. All three motives were important to Henry, and two of them, geography and the crusade, were consonant with the interests of the Middle Ages. The third item, Portuguese nationalism, goes back to the twelfth century in Portugal's separation from Leon-Castile; and though it may be simply another manifestation of the age-old Iberian tendency to localism and particularism, it was a constant force through the medieval history of the Christian kingdoms of the peninsula.

Aside from the medieval elements in Henry's makeup, there was a direct legacy from the Middle Ages in the sciences that fascinated him and whose advancement lay behind the constructive work he patron- ized and furthered. The ideas of cosmography and geography in- herited from the Greeks and transmitted by the second-century Alexandrian Greek Ptolemy were basic for the Middle Ages. To this material, the Arabs added their observation, organization, and specula- tion, both from study of the ancients and from their own travels and practical experience as seafarers. The hold of Ptolemaic theory long tied the hands of cartographers, but with the spreading use of the compass, the Italians of the fourteenth century developed accurate mapping of coast lines and land masses in the remarkable charts fol- lowing the earlier portolani. The Portuguese navigators and their successors had this long medieval accumulation of theory and experi- ence to draw upon in their epoch-making progress. Furthermore, these scientific advances indicate the inaccuracy of the notion that the medieval Church blocked secular and pagan views of the universe and that the cosmology of the schoolmen prevented true scientific de- velopment of astronomy, geography, and related studies. Lest it seem that the cosmographers of the Middle Ages were paragons, however, Haskins' exposition of the persistence of the fabulous and the credu- lity of the best twelfth-century geographers about distant regions must temper overenthusiasm. But empirical data based on discoveries were available for the modern world to correct speculative cosmology.

Before leaving the medieval geographic foundations of fifteenth- and sixteenth-century discoveries, I must mention another medieval contribution. We tend to think of the ocean voyages—perhaps be- cause we owe our European cultural heritage to them and because we use a European language today instead of Comanche—as the sole fac- tor of modern times that should be examined for its medieval ana- logues and ancestry. But there is an important component, too, in the land travels of the Middle Ages. As early as the thirteenth century, Europeans knew of the Far East, and as missionary and trading contacts continued through the next two centuries the wonders of the Orient were part of the lore handed on to the men of the Renaissance. The East was in the minds of the Middle Ages even earlier than the thirteenth century as a result of the two influences of the incursions of Turanian and Mongol warbands and such Christian splinter groups as the Nestorians, the Jacobites, and other churches that had moved eastward from the Mediterranean lands. The Roman Church constantly endeavored to reconvert these heretics to Western orthodoxy, and Catholic missionaries added greatly to European geographical knowledge, as did the great missionary wave of the nineteenth century. The bright hopes of the Latin Church for wholesale conversions in Persia, Turkestan, and China dimmed in the fourteenth and fifteenth centuries with the acceptance of Islam by many of the Mongols and with the spread of the power of the Moslem Ottomans in the Near and Middle East.

It is always fascinating to see a single book exert an overwhelming influence on men. Such was the impact of Marco Polo's *Book of Various Experiences* (or *The Book of Ser Marco Polo, the Venetian,* or *The Travels of Marco Polo,* as later translations and editions have styled it). This book, probably dictated while he was a prisoner of the Genoese after they had defeated the Venetian fleet at the battle of Curzola in 1296, is a colorful narrative and record of observations of the Orient. As a boy of fifteen, in 1271, Marco accompanied his father and uncle on their second trip to the court of the Mongol Great Khan at Peking. From Constantinople they followed the old Byzantine "silk route," long a fixture of trade with the Far East. The Polos were to spend an adventurous twenty-four years before they returned to Venice; and Marco's account of the overland journey through Mesopotamia, Persia, across the "roof of the world" or the Pamirs, the ancient trading cities like Bokhara and Samarkand, the Gobi Desert, and on to modern Peking, gave the West names of places that then and even now evoke mystery and romance, which even the Commissars have not destroyed. Marco's descriptions of the magnificent court and capital of Kublai Khan and of the vastness of China and the richness of its cities did not spare superlatives; they caused the author to be called "il Milione" by Italians critical of his enthusiasm. The young Venetian found favor with Kublai and was sent on missions for the Khan so that he saw many of the cities of the north and south and for three years was governor of Yangchow, a city of a million inhabitants, he says. A week's journey to the south was the old capital of the southern kingdom, the Celestial City Quinsai (modern Hangchow); the description of its glories deeply impressed a Genoese sailor in the service of Castile, and in 1492 he thought he must be near it in the West Indies, though the natives seemed not to have heard of it. Similarly Columbus was struck by Marco's report of the seaports of Kangui and Zayton (modern Canton and Amoy), south of Quinsai, and was convinced that he was approaching them on his first voyage. The Polos found it hard to get the Khan's permission to return home and succeeded only by serving as escorts for a Tartar princess being sent to Khoresm as a bride. This trip was by sea to India and Persia; thence the Polos went to the Black Sea and finally home to Venice. Although part of the route was familiar to the West, Marco's descriptions of the East Indies, Ceylon, India, and the waters and islands he had heard of along the way filled lacunae in Europe's knowledge of those parts of the East.

The influence of Polo's book rose and fell, but its practical effect on the Era of Discovery was to be great. Thanks to the humanists, in the mid-fifteenth century the geography of the ancients, of Strabo and Ptolemy, came to dominate cosmology, and the empirical knowledge of the traders and travelers went into contemporary eclipse. But the discoverers like Columbus and John Cabot sought concrete information about the earth rather than speculative, as did some of the savants like Toscanelli. A copy of Marco Polo possessed by Columbus has survived with the Admiral's marginal notes, showing the influence that book had in the formulation of Columbus' "Enterprise of the Indies." Marco related what he had learned about the island group of Cipango or Japan, whose location he placed 1,500 miles off the coast of Cathay. Both Columbus and Cabot expected to reach this area after a relatively short voyage from Europe. The conclusion Columbus reached—that a westward voyage to Asia was feasible— came from reasonable deductions from the best of medieval authority: the Ptolemaic overestimate of the longitudinal extent of the Eurasian land mass, the Book of Esdras on the proportion of land to water on the earth, the Arab figure on the number of miles to a degree at the equator, Marco Polo's distances and general geography of the Eastern lands and waters, Pierre d'Ailly's *Imago mundi*, and Aeneas Sylvius' *Cosmography*. Thus the discovery of the New World and the opening of all the seaways of the globe were end products of a host of medieval forces, embracing intellectual tradition, observation, practical experience, navigational science, and even religious enthusiasm and desire to win more lands and new souls for Christianity.

It is the fashion today to be concerned with non-Western civilizations and cultures. The developments that I have mentioned show that the men of the Middle Ages had contacts with such cultures. Not only in East Asia and all the vast stretches from China to the Black Sea, but also in Africa, Europeans had experience of other cultures, whether advanced or backward. As a new type of empire, Portuguese and Spanish, developed from the explorations in the sixteenth century, European thought was affected by the very idea of the New World. Unfortunately, few Europeans could then appreciate the advanced elements in the civilizations of the Maya, the Toltec-Aztec, and the Inca. Bishop Landa in Yucatán in 1540 burned all but a few fragments of the Maya books as pagan writings, to our immeasurable loss. But a typical medieval Christian, Isabella the Catholic of Castile, once her theologians had determined that the American Indians were *gente de razón,* that is, that they had souls, decreed that all the natives be converted to Christianity. This and similar laws resulted in the preservation and at least nominal conversion of the native Americans in the Spanish Empire, as the large Indian and Mestizo population of many Latin American nations bears witness today. Bartholomew de Las Casas, coming to Cuba in 1500 as a young planter, underwent a spiritual experience that sent him into holy orders and later into the Dominican Order and made him the lifelong champion of the Indians and their rights. He wrote the *Historia de las Indias,* the best account of Columbus' discovery; and although to awaken the conscience of Spain to the plight of the natives he exaggerated their mistreatment by the Spanish *encomenderos,* he struck one hopeful note—the promise for the future that a previously unknown people had received the gospel of Christ. The pessimism of a strife-torn Europe, which Johan Huizinga stresses in his view of the later Middle Ages, is offset by the extension of European Christendom beyond the seas.

History has no end. Each succeeding generation will learn from the past in order to realize itself and to gain wisdom to meet its own trials. The history of the modern world can have true meaning as it comprehends its medieval past.